OCR Additional Mathematics

REVISION GUIDE

Michael Ling

HODDER
EDUCATION
AN HACHETTE UK COMPANY

Acknowledgements

Exam questions reproduced with the kind permission of OCR.

Hachette UK's policy is to use papers that are natural, renewable and recyclable products and made from wood grown in sustainable forests. The logging and manufacturing processes are expected to conform to the environmental regulations of the country of origin.

Orders: please contact Bookpoint Ltd, 130 Milton Park, Abingdon, Oxon OX14 4SB.
Telephone: (44) 01235 827720. Fax: (44) 01235 400454. Lines are open 9.00–5.00, Monday to Saturday, with a 24-hour message answering service. Visit our website at www.hoddereducation.co.uk

First published in 2012 by
Hodder Education, an Hachette UK company,
338 Euston Road
London NW1 3BH

Impression number 5
Year   2016   2015   2014

Illustrations by Pantek Media, Maidstone, Kent
Typeset in Minion 10.5/14 by Pantek Media, Maidstone, Kent
Printed in India

A catalogue record for this title is available from the British Library

ISBN 978 1444 15475 7

Contents

SECTION 4　CALCULUS

Introduction

Welcome to this Revision Guide, which covers all the topics you might face in an OCR Additional Mathematics exam.

Like the specification, the book is split into four sections: Algebra, Co-ordinate geometry, Trigonometry and Calculus. Each section is split into a number of chapters. The topics covered are summarised in a table at the start of each chapter, which lists the competence statements from the OCR specification. These have each been assigned a code for ease of reference.

Each chapter contains examples and ends with an exercise. You will benefit from working through the examples to help you to understand the topics thoroughly. Then work through the questions in the exercise, consulting the answers if necessary.

Two symbols are used:

 This highlights important points for you to remember.

⚠ This 'warning sign' alerts you to possible pitfalls.

At the end of each section is a selection of questions from past exam papers and other questions of the appropriate standard. Work through these carefully, writing out your answers in full as if you were sitting the exam. Then check them against the worked answers given at the back of the book.

■ Exam technique

For the exam you will be given an answer booklet with space for each part-question. Write each answer in the appropriate space, or it might not be accepted.

There is often more than one way to answer a question, not always of the same length. The space provided will allow for the longest answer, so do not worry if your answer does not take up the full space allowed.

If you need to draw a graph, two grids will be provided. Attempt the question on the first grid. If you are not happy with this answer, you may cross it out and use the second grid. If you do not cross out the first attempt, it will be marked as your answer regardless of what you do on the second grid.

If you are not happy with your first answer to a question, you may cross it out and try again. Write your second attempt either in any remaining space for this part-question or on a separate sheet of paper. Do **not** write it in any space for another part-question. If you do not cross out one attempt, so that the examiner sees two attempts, the answer that is deemed to be your last attempt will be marked even if it is not the better answer.

Check your work carefully. Ask yourself whether each answer seems reasonable and whether any units are needed.

The exam lasts 120 minutes and 100 marks are available.

Some words and phrases used in questions

The wording of the question tells you what kind of answer to give in the exam.

'Write down…'

No working should be necessary.

'State…'

Write down a mathematical fact, possibly adapted to suit the context of the question. No working will be necessary.

'Find…'

The answer will require a little bit of work.

'Calculate…'

Some calculation is required, probably using your calculator. You might be asked to express an answer correct to a number of significant figures or decimal places. If not, write any answers that are approximated so that they are correct to three significant figures.

'Exact…'

Some calculations can be given as exact answers, usually involving a square root or π. A calculator should not be used in these questions to find an approximation because the answer will involve an irrational number.

'Show that…'

You might be given the answer to a part-question because it is needed for a later part of the question and the examiners do not want you to use wrong values, expressions or formulae. In this case, if you write down the answer with no working you will earn **no** marks. Every step, algebraic or arithmetic, must be clearly shown to convince the examiner that you have worked out the answer and not just written it down from the question. Any missing or unconvincing steps will be penalised.

'Hence…'

Answer the question using the result just obtained. Any other method will earn **no** marks.

'Hence or otherwise…'

It is possible to answer the question without using the result just obtained and if you do so full marks will be awarded. But you are advised to answer the question by 'hence'.

'Express…'

A given expression is to be re-written in a different form.

'Sketch…'

This is an instruction to draw the general shape of a curve. It is not so demanding as 'plot', and a grid may not be given. The features of the sketch should include any turning points and the points where the curve cuts the axes.

'Explain…'

A mathematical fact will be given and you are required to say why it is so.

Useful formulae and results

The binomial expansion and the cosine rule are on the formula sheet in the exam. You should learn the others.

Algebra

The remainder theorem	The remainder when a polynomial $f(x)$ is divided by $(x - a)$ is $f(a)$
The factor theorem	If the remainder when $f(x)$ is divided by $(x - a)$ is 0, then $(x - a)$ is a factor of $f(x)$ and $x = a$ is a root of the equation $f(x) = 0$
Solution of quadratic equations	The roots of the quadratic equation $ax^2 + bx + c = 0$ are given by the formula $x = \dfrac{-b \pm \sqrt{b^2 - 4ac}}{2a}$
Binomial expansion	When n is a positive integer, $$(a + b)^n = a^n + \binom{n}{1}a^{n-1}b + \binom{n}{2}a^{n-2}b^2 + \ldots + \binom{n}{r}a^{n-r}b^r + \ldots + b^n$$ where $\binom{n}{r} = {}^nC_r = \dfrac{n!}{r!(n-r)!}$

Co-ordinate geometry

Straight lines	$y = mx + c \qquad y - y_1 = m(x - x_1) \qquad \dfrac{y - y_1}{y_2 - y_1} = \dfrac{x - x_1}{x_2 - x_1}$ Two lines are parallel if $m_1 = m_2$ Two lines are perpendicular if $m_1 \times m_2 = -1$ The distance between two points (x_1, y_1), (x_2, y_2) is $\sqrt{(x_1 - x_2)^2 + (y_1 - y_2)^2}$ The midpoint of two points (x_1, y_1), (x_2, y_2) is at $\left(\dfrac{x_1 + x_2}{2}, \dfrac{y_1 + y_2}{2}\right)$
The circle	The equation $(x - a)^2 + (y - b)^2 = r^2$ represents a circle with centre (a, b) and radius r

Trigonometry

Trigonometric ratios	In a right-angled triangle, $$\sin\theta = \frac{\text{opposite}}{\text{hypotenuse}} \qquad \cos\theta = \frac{\text{adjacent}}{\text{hypotenuse}} \qquad \tan\theta = \frac{\text{opposite}}{\text{adjacent}}$$
Identities	$\tan\theta = \dfrac{\sin\theta}{\cos\theta} \qquad \sin^2\theta + \cos^2\theta = 1$
The sine rule	$\dfrac{a}{\sin A} = \dfrac{b}{\sin B} = \dfrac{c}{\sin C}$
The cosine rule	$a^2 = b^2 + c^2 - 2bc\cos A \qquad \cos A = \dfrac{b^2 + c^2 - a^2}{2bc}$

Calculus

Differentiation	$y = ax^n \quad \Rightarrow \quad \dfrac{dy}{dx} = nax^{n-1}$
Stationary points	These occur when $\dfrac{dy}{dx} = 0$
Area under a curve	The area under the curve $y = f(x)$ between $x = a$ and $x = b$ is $\displaystyle\int_a^b y\,dx$
Kinematics	When there is constant acceleration, $$s = ut + \tfrac{1}{2}at^2 \qquad s = \frac{u + v}{2} \times t \qquad v = u + at \qquad v^2 = u^2 + 2as$$

SECTION 1
Algebra

The skills in algebra developed in this first section underpin all the work in the other three sections of the specification. This first section of the guide helps you to review your algebra skills. It is particularly important that you are proficient in this area if you are to do well.

1 Basic algebra

Manipulation of algebraic expressions	a1	Be able to simplify expressions including algebraic fractions, square roots and polynomials.
	a4	Be confident in the use of brackets.
	a5	Be able to solve a linear equation in one unknown.

Student's Book pages 3–15, 35–42

Algebra is fundamental to higher level mathematics. Skills in the manipulation of algebraic expressions, equations and formulae will enable you to tackle complicated problems with more confidence.

Linear expressions

'Like terms' in an expression should be collected together.

Example: Simplify $a + 2b + 3a - b$.

Answer: $a + 2b + 3a - b = a + 3a + 2b - b = 4a + b$

Every term inside a bracket must be multiplied by the term outside.

Example: Multiply out $2(x + 3) - 4(1 - 2x)$.

Answer: $2(x + 3) - 4(1 - 2x) = 2x + 6 - 4 + 8x$
$$= 10x + 2$$

When multiplying out brackets, everything in one bracket must be multiplied by everything in the other bracket.

Example: Multiply out $(x + 2)(x - 3)$.

Answer: $(x + 2)(x - 3) = x(x - 3) + 2(x - 3)$
$$= x^2 - 3x + 2x - 6$$
$$= x^2 - x - 6$$

When using brackets to simplify expressions, you take a common factor out of each term.

Example: Factorise $3x^2 + 6xy$.

Answer: $3x^2 + 6xy = 3x(x + 2y)$

Multiplying fractions

Look for common factors, which may be numbers, variables or even expressions.

Example: Simplify $\dfrac{2x}{3y} \times \dfrac{6y^2}{x^3}$.

Answer: The factors that can be cancelled are

x giving $\dfrac{2}{3y} \times \dfrac{6y^2}{x^2}$, y giving $\dfrac{2}{3} \times \dfrac{6y}{x^2}$ and 3 giving $\dfrac{2}{1} \times \dfrac{2y}{x^2} = \dfrac{4y}{x^2}$

Adding fractions

As with arithmetic fractions, we need to find a common denominator. This should be the lowest common multiple (LCM) of the denominators.

Example: Simplify $\dfrac{1}{x-1} + \dfrac{2}{x-2}$.

Answer: The LCM is the product of the denominators, i.e. $(x - 1)(x - 2)$.

$$\Rightarrow \quad \frac{1}{x-1} \times \frac{x-2}{x-2} + \frac{2}{x-2} \times \frac{x-1}{x-1} = \frac{(x-2) + 2(x-1)}{(x-1)(x-2)}$$
$$= \frac{3x-4}{(x-1)(x-2)}$$

Solving linear equations

Equations can be solved by manipulating both sides in the same way, using the skills outlined above.

Example: Solve $3x + 4 = 12 - x$.

Answer: Add x to both sides: $\qquad 4x + 4 = 12$
Subtract 4 from both sides: $\qquad 4x = 8$
Divide both sides by 4: $\qquad x = 2$

Example: Solve the equation $\dfrac{x - 2}{3} + 1 = \dfrac{x}{2}$.

Answer: The LCM is 6, so multiply throughout by 6.

$$\Rightarrow \quad 2(x - 2) + 6 = 3x$$
$$\Rightarrow \quad 2x - 4 + 6 = 3x$$
$$\Rightarrow \quad -4 + 6 = 3x - 2x$$
$$\Rightarrow \quad x = 2$$

Changing the subject of a formula

Manipulate the formula in the same way as for equations so that the required variable is the 'subject'. C is the subject of the formula if the formula can be written $C = \ldots$

Example: Make h the subject of the formula $A = \frac{1}{2}(a + b)h$.

Answer: $\qquad A = \frac{1}{2}(a + b)h$
$$\Rightarrow \quad 2A = (a + b)h$$
$$\Rightarrow \quad h = \frac{2A}{a + b}$$

⚠ Take care over signs when removing brackets, e.g. $x - (y - z) = x - y + z$.

✪ ■ The same operation must be applied to both sides of an equation when finding a solution.
■ When adding and multiplying algebraic fractions, use the same techniques as for arithmetic.

Exercise 1.1

1 Simplify the following expressions.

(i) $3x - y - x + 2y$ 　　　(ii) $2x + 2y - (2y + x)$ 　　　(iii) $2x + 3y - 2x + 3y$

2 Multiply out the following expressions.

(i) $2(a + 2b) + 3(2a - b)$ 　　　(ii) $x(x + 10) + 2x(x - 1)$ 　　　(iii) $(x - 1)(2x + 3)$

3 Factorise the following expressions.

(i) $2x + 4y$ 　　　(ii) $x^2 + 3xy$ 　　　(iii) $2xy^2 + 6x^2y$

4 Simplify the following expressions.

(i) $\dfrac{2x^2}{3y} \times \dfrac{9y^2}{8xy}$ 　　　(ii) $\dfrac{2}{x + 1} - \dfrac{3}{x + 2}$

5 Make a the subject of the formula $s = ut + \frac{1}{2}at^2$.

6 Solve the following equations for x.

(i) $2(x - 1) = 4 - 3x$ 　　　(ii) $\dfrac{2(x - 1)}{3} = 1 + x$ 　　　(iii) $\dfrac{x}{3} + \dfrac{x - 1}{4} = \dfrac{1}{6}$

2 Quadratic equations

Solution of equations	a6	Be able to solve quadratic equations by factorisation, the use of the formula and by completing the square.

Student's Book pages 16–23

The solution of a quadratic equation may take three forms. There may be two real roots or none. Additionally, the roots may be 'coincident'.

Solving quadratic equations that factorise

You may meet two situations for the quadratic equation $ax^2 + bx + c = 0$.

The first situation is that $a = 1$. So the quadratic equation has the form $x^2 + bx + c = 0$. If it factorises then it takes the form $(x - k)(x - l) = 0$.

Since this expands to give $x^2 - (k + l)x + kl = 0$, it follows that the two numbers k and l must

- multiply to give the constant term in the function, and
- add to give the coefficient of the x term.

Example: Solve the equation $x^2 - 11x + 18 = 0$.

Answer: Two factors of 18 that sum to give −11 are −2 and −9.

$$\Rightarrow \qquad x^2 - 2x - 9x + 18 = 0$$
$$\Rightarrow \quad x(x - 2) - 9(x - 2) = 0$$
$$\Rightarrow \qquad\qquad (x - 9)(x - 2) = 0$$
$$\Rightarrow \quad x = 9 \text{ or } x = 2$$

In the second situation, $a \neq 1$. Here you need two numbers that

- multiply to give the product of the constant term and the coefficient of x^2, and
- add to give the coefficient of the x term.

Example: Solve the equation $6x^2 - 17x + 12 = 0$.

Answer: The product of the x^2 coefficient and the constant term is $6 \times 12 = 72$.
Two factors of 72 that sum to give −17 are −9 and −8.

$$\Rightarrow \qquad\quad 6x^2 - 9x - 8x + 12 = 0$$
$$\Rightarrow \quad 3x(2x - 3) - 4(2x - 3) = 0$$
$$\Rightarrow \qquad\qquad\quad (3x - 4)(2x - 3) = 0$$
$$\Rightarrow \quad x = \frac{4}{3} \text{ or } x = \frac{3}{2}$$

Solving quadratic equations that do not factorise

The formula for solving the quadratic equation $ax^2 + bx + c = 0$ is $x = \dfrac{-b \pm \sqrt{b^2 - 4ac}}{2a}$.
Roots should be given to 3 significant figures.

Example: Solve the equation $x^2 - 2x - 5 = 0$.

Answer: In the formula, $a = 1$, $b = -2$, $c = -5$.

$$\Rightarrow \quad x = \frac{2 \pm \sqrt{4 + 20}}{2}$$
$$= \frac{2 \pm \sqrt{24}}{2}$$
$$= \frac{2 \pm 4.899}{2}$$
$$\Rightarrow \quad x = 3.45 \text{ or } x = -1.45$$

Completing the square

Completing the square involves writing the equation in the form $(x - k)^2 = m$.

An equation in this form can be solved by taking the square root of each side, giving $x - k = \pm\sqrt{m}$. k is half the coefficient of the x term in the equation $\left(\text{i.e. } k = \frac{1}{2}b\right)$.

Example: Solve the equation $x^2 - 4x - 7 = 0$.

Answer: $x^2 - 4x - 7 = 0$

$\Rightarrow \quad (x - 2)^2 - 4 - 7 = 0$

$\Rightarrow \qquad\qquad (x - 2)^2 = 11$

$\Rightarrow \qquad\qquad\quad x - 2 = \pm\sqrt{11}$

$\Rightarrow \qquad\qquad\qquad x = 2 \pm \sqrt{11}$

The minimum or maximum value of a quadratic expression can be found by completing the square.

Example: Find the minimum value of $f(x) = x^2 - 4x + 7$.

Answer: $x^2 - 4x + 7 = x^2 - 4x + 4 + 3$

$\qquad\qquad\qquad = (x - 2)^2 + 3$

Since the minimum value of the squared term is 0 (when $x = 2$), the minimum value of $f(x)$ is 3.

⚠ ■ The formula for the solution of a quadratic equation is **not** given on the formulae page of the exam paper, so it needs to be learned. Make sure that when you write it down you do so accurately.

■ Do not use the formula for solving quadratic equations if you do not need to. For instance, the equation $x^2 - 2x = 0$ can be solved by factorisation.

✪ ■ The function $f(x) = (x - a)^2 + b$ has a minimum value of b when $x = a$.

■ The solutions of the quadratic equation $ax^2 + bx + c = 0$ are $x = \dfrac{-b \pm \sqrt{b^2 - 4ac}}{2a}$ if $b^2 - 4ac \geqslant 0$

Exercise 1.2

1 Solve the following quadratic equations by factorisation.

(i) $x^2 + 3x - 10 = 0$

(ii) $x^2 - 3x - 4 = 0$

(iii) $x^2 - 6x + 5 = 0$

2 Solve the following quadratic equations by using the formula. Give your roots to 3 significant figures.

(i) $x^2 - 3x - 8 = 0$

(ii) $x^2 - 2x - 5 = 0$

(iii) $x^2 + 4x - 1 = 0$

3 Express $f(x) = x^2 + 6x + 10$ in the form $(x + a)^2 + b$, where a and b are integers. Hence show that the equation $f(x) = 0$ has no real roots.

4 Solve the following quadratic equations.

(i) $8x^2 - 22x + 5 = 0$

(ii) $2x^2 + 3x - 4 = 0$

5 Express $f(x) = 2 + 4x - x^2$ in the form $k - (x - a)^2$.
Hence find the maximum value of $f(x)$ and the value of x when this occurs.

Simultaneous equations

Solution of equations	a8	Be able to solve two linear simultaneous equations in two unknowns.
	a9	Be able to solve two simultaneous equations in two unknowns where one equation is linear and the other is quadratic.

Student's Book pages 23–30

Simultaneous equations are two equations that are satisfied at the same time. If the equations are both linear, then there is one co-ordinate pair that satisfies them. If one equation is quadratic, then there will generally be two co-ordinate pairs that satisfy both.

Two linear equations can be solved either by elimination or by substitution. If one is linear and one is quadratic, then they must be solved by substitution.

Two linear equations

Two equations can be solved by elimination.

> **Example:** Solve simultaneously the following equations.
>
> $$2x + 3y = 11 \qquad ①$$
> $$7x - y = 4 \qquad ②$$
>
> **Answer:** Multiply ② by 3:
> $$2x + 3y = 11 \qquad ①$$
> $$21x - 3y = 12 \qquad ③$$
> Add ① and ③: $\qquad 23x = 23 \quad \Rightarrow \quad x = 1$
> Substitute into ①: $\qquad 2 + 3y = 11 \quad \Rightarrow \quad y = 3$
> The solution is $x = 1$, $y = 3$.

Two equations can be solved by substitution.

> **Example:** Solve simultaneously the following equations.
>
> $$2x + 3y = 11 \qquad ①$$
> $$7x - y = 4 \qquad ②$$
>
> **Answer:** Make y the subject in ②: $y = 7x - 4 \qquad ③$
> Substitute into ①: $\qquad 2x + 3(7x - 4) = 11$
> $$\Rightarrow \quad 2x + 21x - 12 = 11$$
> $$\Rightarrow \quad 23x = 23$$
> $$\Rightarrow \quad x = 1$$
> Substitute into ①: $\qquad 2 + 3y = 11$
> $$\Rightarrow \quad y = 3$$
> The solution is $x = 1$, $y = 3$.

Simultaneous equations when one equation is quadratic

These equations have to be solved by substitution. Make one of the variables the subject of the linear equation and substitute into the quadratic.

Example: Solve the simultaneous equations $3x - y = 3$ and $y = x^2 + 4x - 9$.

Answer: Make y the subject of the first equation: $y = 3x - 3$

Substitute into the second equation:

$$3x - 3 = x^2 + 4x - 9$$
$$\Rightarrow \quad x^2 + x - 6 = 0$$
$$\Rightarrow \quad (x + 3)(x - 2) = 0$$
$$\Rightarrow \quad x = -3 \text{ or } x = 2$$
$$x = -3 \quad \Rightarrow \quad y = -12 \text{ and } x = 2 \quad \Rightarrow \quad y = 3$$

The solution is $x = -3$, $y = -12$ and $x = 2$, $y = 3$.

Sometimes the substitution will involve fractions. In these situations, be careful about making one letter the subject and how you substitute. There will be fewer opportunities for algebraic and arithmetic error if y is made the subject.

Example: Solve the simultaneous equations $2x + 3y = 8$ and $y = x^2 + 2x - 1$.

Answer: Make y the subject of the first equation: $y = \dfrac{8 - 2x}{3}$

Substitute into the second equation: $\dfrac{8 - 2x}{3} = x^2 + 2x - 1$

$$\Rightarrow \quad 8 - 2x = 3x^2 + 6x - 3$$
$$\Rightarrow \quad 3x^2 + 8x - 11 = 0$$

Factors of $3 \times -11 = -33$ that sum to give 8 are 11 and -3

$$\Rightarrow \quad 3x^2 + 11x - 3x - 11 = 0$$
$$\Rightarrow \quad x(3x + 11) - 1(3x + 11) = 0$$
$$\Rightarrow \quad (x - 1)(3x + 11) = 0$$
$$\Rightarrow \quad x = 1 \text{ or } x = -\tfrac{11}{3}$$

Substitute into the rearranged first equation:

$$x = 1 \quad \Rightarrow \quad y = \frac{8 - 2}{3} = 2$$

$$x = -\tfrac{11}{3} \quad \Rightarrow \quad y = \frac{8 + \frac{22}{3}}{3} = \frac{\frac{46}{3}}{3} = \frac{46}{9}$$

The solution is $x = 1$, $y = 2$ and $x = -\tfrac{11}{3}$, $y = \tfrac{46}{9}$.

- ■ Linear equations can be solved by substitution or elimination. Equations where one is quadratic have to be solved by substitution.
- ■ When making one variable the subject of the linear equation in order to substitute, it does not matter which variable you choose. In general, however, one will be easier than the other. Try to avoid fractions if possible.

Exercise 1.3

1 Solve simultaneously the equations $3x - y = 9$ and $5x + 3y = 1$.

2 Solve by substitution the simultaneous equations $y = 3x - 7$ and $4x + 3y = 18$.

3 Solve simultaneously the equations $2y + x = 15$ and $x^2 + y^2 = 50$.

4 Find the points of intersection of the line $y = 2x + 1$ with the circle $x^2 + y^2 = 20$, giving your answers correct to 2 decimal places.

4 Setting up equations

Solution of equations	a10	Be able to set up and solve problems leading to linear, quadratic and cubic equations in one unknown, and to simultaneous linear equations in two unknowns.

Student's Book pages 6–9, 16–30

You learn algebra in order to solve problems! A problem will be given in words and you need to be able to set up the equation in order to solve it. You will then need to give the solution to the problem.

The Student's Book does not have a specific section on this competence statement; the work is embedded in the sections on solving equations.

Setting up linear equations

A problem will be given in words. The first step of your solution will always be 'Let x be …' where this is the unknown to be found. The last line is **not** '$x = …$' as this is the solution to your equation and not the solution to the problem!

Example: Mr Smith is 5 years older than his wife and was 26 when their twins were born. The total sum of their ages this year is 91. Find the age of each member of the family.

Answer: Let Mr Smith's age be x. Then Mrs Smith is aged $x - 5$ and the twins are aged $x - 26$. The total age is 91. So

$$x + x - 5 + 2(x - 26) = 91$$
$$\Rightarrow \qquad 4x - 57 = 91$$
$$\Rightarrow \qquad 4x = 148$$
$$\Rightarrow \qquad x = 37$$

Mr Smith is aged 37, Mrs Smith is 32 and the twins are 11.

Setting up quadratic equations

Certain problems will lead to a quadratic equation, particularly when the statement of the problem in algebraic terms includes fractions. The process is the same.

Example: A farmer has 20 metres of fencing. She wants to enclose a rectangular area of $42\,m^2$ using the fencing for three sides and a long wall for the other side. What should be the dimensions of the rectangle?

Answer: Let x be the length of the two equal sides.
Then the length of the third side is $20 - 2x$.
Since the area is to be $42\,m^2$, this gives

$$x(20 - 2x) = 42$$
$$\Rightarrow \qquad 20x - 2x^2 = 42$$
$$\Rightarrow \qquad x^2 - 10x + 21 = 0$$
$$\Rightarrow \qquad (x - 7)(x - 3) = 0$$

So $x = 3$ or $x = 7$
If $x = 3$ then the sides are 3 m, 3 m and 14 m.
If $x = 7$ then the sides are 7 m, 7 m, and 6 m.
Both give an area of $42\,m^2$.

In some problems one of the answers may be impossible, so both have to be checked.

Example: A group of children share 120 sweets. If there had been 4 fewer children then each child would have got 5 more sweets. How many children are there and how many sweets did they each receive?

Answer: Let x be the number of children. Then the number of sweets each receives is $\dfrac{120}{x}$.

If there were $x - 4$ children, each would receive $\dfrac{120}{x-4}$ sweets, which is 5 more.

$$\Rightarrow \qquad \qquad \qquad \frac{120}{x} + 5 = \frac{120}{x-4}$$
$$\Rightarrow \qquad 120(x-4) + 5x(x-4) = 120x$$
$$\Rightarrow \qquad \qquad 5x^2 - 20x - 480 = 0$$
$$\Rightarrow \qquad \qquad \qquad x^2 - 4x - 96 = 0$$
$$\Rightarrow \qquad \qquad \quad (x-12)(x+8) = 0$$
$$\Rightarrow \qquad \quad x = 12 \text{ or } x = -8$$

Reject the second value as you cannot have a negative number of children.
So there were 12 children and each had 10 sweets.
(Check: 4 fewer children means 8 children, who would then get 15 sweets.)

Setting up simultaneous equations

This will be needed when there are two unknowns. To solve the problem you will be given two different statements. You will need to use two variables.

Example: At an interval during a concert John buys 3 coffees and 5 ice creams for his party. The total cost is £14.10. A few days later he buys 4 coffees and one ice cream and the cost is £10.30. Find the price of a coffee and the price of an ice cream.

Answer: Let the price of a coffee be x pence and the price of an ice cream be y pence.
Then on the first occasion $3x + 5y = 1410$ ①
On the second occasion $4x + y = 1030$ ②
$5 \times ② - ① \quad \Rightarrow \quad 17x = 3740$
$$\Rightarrow \qquad x = 220$$
$$\Rightarrow \qquad y = 150$$
So the price of a coffee is £2.20 and the price of an ice cream is £1.50.

⭐ ■ In setting up an equation you need to let a letter stand for the unknown quantity. So your first line should be 'Let $x = \ldots$' or equivalent.
■ If you are setting up equations with two unknowns then let x be one value and y the other.

 You should state the answer to the problem at the end, not just the value of the unknown variable(s).

Exercise 1.4

1 The second angle in a triangle is 10° more than the first angle. The third angle is 20° more than the first one. Find the sizes of the three angles of the triangle.

2 The first prize in a competition is £6000. Two groups of friends enter the competition. The second group has two more members than the first. Both groups will share the prize equally amongst the members of their own group if they win. If the second group wins, each member will receive £500 less than each member of the first group would if they won. Let x be the number of people in the smaller group. Set up an equation in x and show that it reduces to $x^2 + 2x - 24 = 0$. Solve this equation to find the number of people in each group.

3 John drives along a straight motorway at a constant speed for 120 kilometres. The next day he completes the same journey travelling at 10 km/h faster. He completes this journey in 10 minutes less than the first journey. Find the two speeds at which he travelled.

4 Joe buys 2 packets of biscuits and 3 bottles of drink. The total cost is £7.44. Jane buys 5 packets of the same biscuits and 2 bottles of the same drink and her bill comes to £8.81. Find the price of a packet of biscuits and the price of a bottle of drink.

5 Inequalities

| Inequalities | a11 | Be able to manipulate inequalities. |
| | a12 | Be able to solve linear and quadratic inequalities algebraically and graphically. |

Student's Book pages 32–35

Inequalities can be manipulated in the same way as equations except for one rule: if both sides are multiplied or divided by a negative number, then the direction of the inequality changes.

Linear inequalities

Remembering the above rule, linear inequalities can be solved in the same way as equations.

> **Example:** Solve the inequality $3x + 15 < 1 - 4x$.
>
> **Answer:** Add $4x$ to both sides: $\qquad 7x + 15 < 1$
> Subtract 15 from both sides: $\qquad 7x < -14$
> Divide both sides by 7: $\qquad x < -2$

Quadratic inequalities

A quadratic inequality takes the form $f(x) < 0$ (with any of the four inequality signs), or can be manipulated into that form, where $f(x)$ can be factorised.

When $f(x)$ is factorised you have two expressions whose product satisfies the inequality. You can then use the facts that positive × positive = positive, negative × negative = positive, and positive × negative = negative.

> **Example:** Solve the inequality $x^2 - 4x - 32 < 0$.
>
> **Answer:** First factorise the expression: $(x - 8)(x + 4) < 0$.
> Because the product is less than 0 (i.e. negative) then one of the two factors is negative and the other is positive.
> That is, either $(x - 8) < 0$ and $(x + 4) > 0$, or $(x - 8) < 0$ and $(x + 4) < 0$.
> If $x = 8$ or $x = -4$, the product will be 0, so look at the signs either side of these critical values.
>
> | | $x < -4$ | $-4 < x < 8$ | $x > 8$ |
> |---|---|---|---|
> | **sign of $(x - 8)$** | – | – | + |
> | **sign of $(x + 4)$** | – | + | + |
> | **sign of $(x - 8)(x + 4)$** | + | – | + |
>
> So the solution to $(x - 8)(x + 4) < 0$ is $-4 < x < 8$.

Solving quadratic inequalities graphically

The graph represents the function $y = f(x) = ax^2 + bx + c$, where $a > 0$.

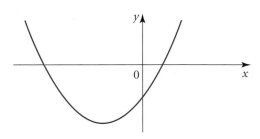

If f(x) < 0 then the range of values of x is the range where the graph is below the x-axis.

If f(x) ⩾ 0 then the range of values of x is the range where the graph is on or above the x-axis.

Note that different circles are used to indicate whether or not an end point is included in an inequality range. If the end point is included in the range then the circle is drawn solid. If it is not included then the circle is drawn open.

Using square roots

The square root of an integer is either also an integer or it is irrational. The word 'irrational' is used to describe a number that cannot be expressed as a fraction. So, written as a decimal, it does not terminate and does not recur. Finding the value of a square root, therefore, means that only an approximation can be given. π is an irrational number and so is $\sqrt{2}$.

For example, $\sqrt{4} = 2$, $\sqrt{25} = 5$, $\sqrt{29} = 5.385...$

You will sometimes be asked to write down an exact value. In these cases you should **not** use your calculator to approximate your answer but instead leave the answer including square roots.

You should always simplify a square root as far as possible by taking out any factors that are perfect squares.

Example: Simplify $\sqrt{8}$.

Answer: $\sqrt{8} = \sqrt{4 \times 2} = \sqrt{4} \times \sqrt{2} = 2\sqrt{2}$

You should not leave your answer with a square root in the denominator.

Example: Simplify $\dfrac{3}{\sqrt{2}}$.

Answer: $\dfrac{3}{\sqrt{2}} = \dfrac{3}{\sqrt{2}} \times \dfrac{\sqrt{2}}{\sqrt{2}} = \dfrac{3\sqrt{2}}{2}$

Example: Solve the quadratic equation $x^2 + 4x - 7 = 0$, giving your answers exactly.

Answer: Using the formula:

$$x = \frac{-4 \pm \sqrt{16 + 28}}{2} = \frac{-4 \pm \sqrt{44}}{2} = \frac{-4 \pm \sqrt{4 \times 11}}{2} = \frac{-4 \pm 2\sqrt{11}}{2} = -2 \pm \sqrt{11}$$

$$\Rightarrow \quad x = -2 + \sqrt{11} \quad \text{or} \quad x = -2 - \sqrt{11}$$

- Solving inequalities is the same as solving equations unless you divide or multiply by a negative number. If you do, then you must reverse the inequality.
- To solve a quadratic inequality with terms on both sides, first collect all the terms on to one side.
- To solve a quadratic inequality, sketch a graph of the function and use the points of intersection with the x-axis to give the solution.

Exercise 1.5

1 Solve the inequality $2x + 1 > 5$.

2 Solve the inequality $1 - 3x > x + 2$.

3 Solve the inequality $x^2 + 2x - 8 > 0$.

6 Polynomials

The remainder theorem	a2	Be able to find the remainder of a polynomial up to order 3 when divided by a linear factor.
The factor theorem	a3	Be able to find linear factors of a polynomial up to order 3.
Solution of equations	a7	Be able to solve a cubic equation by factorisation.

Student's Book pages 45–58

A polynomial is a number of terms of the form ax^n added or subtracted, where n is a positive integer. In this specification, the highest value of n is 3. So a polynomial is a cubic, quadratic or linear function of x.

Addition and subtraction of polynomials

Polynomials are added and subtracted by collecting 'like terms'. In this situation, like terms are those with the same power.

Example: Add $(3x^3 - 2x^2 + 3x - 4)$ to $(x^3 + 3x^2 + 2x - 4)$.

Answer:
$$(3x^3 - 2x^2 + 3x - 4) + (x^3 + 3x^2 + 2x - 4)$$
$$= 3x^3 + x^3 - 2x^2 + 3x^2 + 3x + 2x - 4 - 4$$
$$= 4x^3 + x^2 + 5x - 8$$

Multiplication of polynomials

Multiplying out two polynomials is the same process as multiplying out two linear expressions – everything in one bracket is multiplied by everything in the other.

Example: Multiply $(x^2 - 3x + 4)$ by $(2x - 3)$.

Answer:
$$(x^2 - 3x + 4) \times (2x - 3)$$
$$= x^2(2x - 3) - 3x(2x - 3) + 4(2x - 3)$$
$$= 2x^3 - 3x^2 - 6x^2 + 9x + 8x - 12$$
$$= 2x^3 - 9x^2 + 17x - 12$$

Division of polynomials

As with numbers, when one polynomial is divided into another it 'goes' a number of times, leaving a remainder. If the remainder is 0, then the polynomial divides exactly and is called a factor.

Example: Divide $(x^3 - 3x^2 + 4x - 1)$ by $(x - 1)$.

Answer:

$$
\begin{array}{r}
x^2 - 2x + 2 \\
x - 1 \overline{)\, x^3 - 3x^2 + 4x - 1} \\
\underline{x^3 - x^2} \\
-2x^2 + 4x \\
\underline{-2x^2 + 2x} \\
2x - 1 \\
\underline{2x - 2} \\
1
\end{array}
$$

The remainder is 1.

The remainder theorem

If f(x) is a polynomial, then when f(x) is divided by ($x - a$) the remainder is f(a).

> **Example:** Find the remainder when ($x^3 - 3x^2 + x - 3$) is divided by ($x - 2$).
>
> **Answer:** The remainder is f(2) = 8 − 12 + 2 − 3 = −5.

The factor theorem

If the remainder when f(x) is divided by ($x - a$) is 0, then ($x - a$) is a factor of f(x).

> **Example:** Show that ($x + 2$) is a factor of f(x) = $x^3 + 2x^2 - x - 2$.
>
> **Answer:** f(−2) = −8 + 8 + 2 − 2 = 0, so ($x + 2$) is a factor.

Solving a cubic equation by factorisation

The integer roots of a cubic equation can be found by trial using the factor theorem. If there are three roots to be found then all three can be found by trial, or once one has been found the associated factor may be divided into the cubic function leaving a quadratic. This can then be factorised.

If the roots are a, b and c then the constant number in the function is $-abc$.

> **Example:** Solve the equation f(x) = $x^3 - 4x^2 + x + 6 = 0$.
>
> **Answer:** Remember that each root is a factor of 6.
> By trial: f(2) = 8 − 16 + 2 + 6 = 0,
> so ($x - 2$) is a factor of f(x) and $x = 2$ is a root of the equation f(x) = 0.
> Similarly, f(3) = 27 − 36 + 3 + 6 = 0, so $x = 3$ is a root.
> Since 2 × 3 × −1 = −6, the third root must be $x = -1$.
> The solution is $x = -1$, $x = 2$ or $x = 3$.

⚠ If you are only asked for the remainder when one polynomial is divided by another, then use the remainder theorem and **not** long division.

✪ ■ The remainder when f(x) is divided by ($x - a$) is f(a). The remainder when f(x) is divided by ($x + a$) is f($-a$).

■ If f(a) = 0 then ($x - a$) is a factor of f(x) and $x = a$ is a root of the equation f(x) = 0.

Exercise 1.6

1 (i) Add ($x^3 + x^2 - 2x + 3$) to ($x^2 - 2x - 1$).

(ii) Subtract ($x^3 - x + 1$) from ($2x^3 + 2x^2 - 3x + 1$).

(iii) Simplify ($x^3 + 2x^2 + 5$) + ($x^3 + x^2 + 3x + 1$) − ($x^2 - 2x - 3$).

2 Multiply ($x^2 - 3x + 2$) by ($2x + 3$).

3 Divide ($x^3 + 2x^2 + 2x - 3$) by ($x + 1$). $x^2 + x - 1$ with remainder -4.

4 Find the remainder when f(x) = $x^3 - 2x^2 + x + 4$ is divided by

(i) ($x - 2$)   6

(ii) ($x + 2$).   2

5 (i) Show that ($x - 2$) is a factor of f(x) = $x^3 + x^2 - 4x - 4$.

(ii) Show that ($x + 1$) is a factor of f(x) = $x^3 + x^2 + x + 1$.

6 Use the factor theorem to solve the equation $x^3 - 3x^2 - x + 3 = 0$. f(1) = 0
so ($x-1$) is a factor
of f(x) and $x=1$ is
a root of equation f(x)=0.

The binomial expansion

The binomial expansion	a13	Understand and be able to apply the binomial expansion of $(a + b)^n$ where n is a positive integer.
Application to probability	a14	Recognise probability situations which give rise to the binomial distribution.
	a15	Be able to identify the binomial parameter, p, the probability of success.
	a16	Be able to calculate probabilities using the binomial distribution.

Student's Book pages 61–70

The binomial expansion is the expansion of an expression such as $(a + b)^n$, where n is a positive integer. When a and b are the probabilities of success and failure of an event respectively, then each term of the expansion represents the probability of a particular number of successes in n independent and identical events.

The binomial expansion

When $(a + b)^n$ is expanded, the first term is a^n, the last is b^n and the middle terms take the form $\binom{n}{r} a^{n-r} b^r$. The powers of a and b sum to n and $\binom{n}{r}$ is the coefficient.

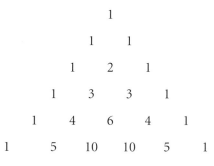

$$\binom{n}{r} = {}^nC_r = \frac{n!}{(n-r)!r!}$$

The coefficients

The coefficients in the expansion can be found in three ways.

The first way, when many or all of the terms are required and n is not too large, is to use Pascal's triangle.

```
                    1
                 1     1
              1     2     1
           1     3     3     1
        1     4     6     4     1
     1     5     10    10    5     1
  etc.
```

Each coefficient can be generated by adding the two above, as shown.

> **Example:** Expand $(2 + x)^5$.
>
> **Answer:** The coefficients are obtained from the row of Pascal's triangle that starts 1, 5…
> $$(2 + x)^5 = 2^5 + 5 \times 2^4 \times x + 10 \times 2^3 \times x^2 + 10 \times 2^2 \times x^3 + 5 \times 2^1 \times x^4 + x^5$$
> $$= 32 + 80x + 80x^2 + 40x^3 + 10x^4 + x^5$$

The second way, which is always valid, is to use the formula $\binom{n}{r} = {}^nC_r = \frac{n!}{r!(n-r)!}$. For $r = 1, 2, 3 \ldots$ the coefficients are

$$1, \quad \frac{n}{1}, \quad \frac{n(n-1)}{1 \times 2}, \quad \frac{n(n-1)(n-2)}{1 \times 2 \times 3}, \quad \ldots$$

The third way is to use the ${}^nC_r$ button on your calculator.

Example: Find the first four terms of the expansion $(1 - 2x)^8$.

Answer: $(1 - 2x)^8 = 1 + \dfrac{8}{1}(-2x) + \dfrac{8 \times 7}{1 \times 2}(-2x)^2 + \dfrac{8 \times 7 \times 6}{1 \times 2 \times 3}(-2x)^3 + \dots$

$= 1 - 8 \times 2x + 28 \times 4x^2 - 56 \times 8x^3 + \dots$

$= 1 - 16x + 112x^2 - 448x^3 + \dots$

The first four terms are 1, $-16x$, $112x^2$ and $-448x^3$.

The binomial distribution

The binomial distribution arises when there are a number of events. For each event only two outcomes are possible, success or failure. If the probability of success, $P(S) = p$ and the probability of failure, $P(F) = q$, then $p + q = 1$. Each event is independent of the others and $P(S)$ is constant. p is called the binomial parameter.

For a binomial distribution with n events, $P(r$ successes$)$ is given by the appropriate term in the binomial expansion $(p + q)^n$.

Example: The probability of obtaining a head when a coin is tossed is $\frac{1}{2}$. If the coin is tossed 10 times, what is the probability that all 10 results are heads?

Answer: Each toss is independent of the others, so the probability of obtaining 10 heads is $\left(\frac{1}{2}\right)^{10}$.

Example: A spinner has five sides, numbered 1 to 5. When it is spun, each side is equally likely to come to rest on the table. What is the probability that the side with number 5 lands on the table exactly three times in five spins?

Answer: Because each side is equally likely to rest on the table, $p = \frac{1}{5}$ and $q = \frac{4}{5}$.

$P(3$ successes$)$ is given by the third term in the expansion of $(p + q)^5$.

$\Rightarrow \quad P(3 \text{ successes}) = 10\left(\frac{1}{5}\right)^3\left(\frac{4}{5}\right)^2 = 10 \times \dfrac{16}{5^5} = \dfrac{32}{625} = 0.0512$

Example: A normal die is thrown three times. What is the probability of getting at least one six?

Answer: $P(\text{at least one six}) = 1 - P(\text{no six}) = 1 - \left(\frac{1}{6}\right)^3 = 1 - 0.0046 = 0.995$

⚠ If you are asked for the first three or four terms of an expansion only, then use the ^nC_r method to find the coefficients. Creating Pascal's triangle can take time and most of it will not be used.

 ■ If an event has two possible outcomes, success or failure, with probabilities p and q respectively, then $p + q = 1$.
■ If there are n events that are independent and have the same probability, p, of success, then the probability of r successes is $\dbinom{n}{r}p^r q^{n-r}$. Note that the sum of powers in this term is n, and the inclusion of a coefficient.
■ In an experiment with n independent events, each with probability p of success, then $P(\text{at least one success}) = 1 - P(0 \text{ successes})$.

Exercise 1.7

1 Write down the first four terms in the expansion of $(1 + x)^6$.

2 Find the constant term in the expansion of $\left(x - \dfrac{1}{x}\right)^4$.

3 Find the probability of obtaining exactly two sixes when a normal die is thrown five times.

4 A factory has three machines that work at the same time. Each machine works independently of the others and the probability that it will break down on any given day is 0.1. Any machine that breaks down is not used again that day and is mended and serviced overnight. In any given day, what is the probability that at least one machine is working at the end of the day?

1 Solve the following equations. Give your answers correct to three decimal places.

(i) $\dfrac{2(x-1)}{3} - 2 = \dfrac{3x+1}{4}$ [3]

(ii) $x^2 - 4x - 7 = 0$ [4]

2 Solve the following inequalities.

(i) $3 - x > 5(x+1)$ [3]

(ii) $x^2 - 5x < 6$ [4]

3 (i) Express $f(x) = x^2 - 6x - 10$ in the form $(x+a)^2 + b$ where a and b are integers. [3]

Hence

(ii) write down the minimum value of $f(x)$ and the value of x at which it occurs [2]

(iii) solve the equation $f(x) = 0$. [3]

4 Solve simultaneously the equations $y = x + 6$ and $y = x^2 - x + 3$. [4]

[OCR 2003 Q1]

5 The function $f(x)$ is defined by $f(x) = x^3 + 2x^2 - 5x - 6$.

(i) Show that when $f(x)$ is divided by $(x - 3)$ the remainder is 24. [2]

(ii) Show that $(x - 2)$ is a factor of $f(x)$. [1]

(iii) Hence solve the equation $f(x) = 0$. [4]

[OCR 2003 Q9]

6 (i) Expand $(2 + x)^7$ in ascending powers of x up to and including the term in x^3. [4]

(ii) Use your expansion with an appropriate value of x to find an approximate value of 1.99^7.
Give your answer to 4 decimal places.
Show your working clearly, giving the numerical value of each term.
(Writing down the value of 1.99^7 from your calculator will earn no mark.) [3]

[OCR 2003 Q6]

7 I regularly travel a journey of 200 kilometres. When I travel by day I average v kilometres per hour. When I travel at night the traffic is not so bad, so I can average 20 kilometres per hour faster. This means that I am able to complete the journey in 50 minutes less time.

(i) Write down expressions for the journey times during the day and at night. [2]

(ii) Hence form an equation in v and show that it simplifies to

$$v^2 + 20v - 4800 = 0.$$ [5]

(iii) Hence find the times it takes me to complete the journey during the day and at night. [5]

[OCR 2004 Q13]

8 In a game, 5 normal dice are rolled.
What is the probability that

(i) no sixes are rolled [2]

(ii) at least 1 six is rolled [3]

(iii) exactly 3 sixes are rolled? [4]

SECTION 2
Co-ordinate geometry

Co-ordinate geometry deals with points, lines and curves described on a co-ordinate axis system, usually x- and y-axes, which are perpendicular. A point is then described uniquely by a 'co-ordinate pair'. Equations of lines and curves represent the connection between the x and y co-ordinates for all points on the line or curve.

1 Straight lines

The straight line	g1	Know the definition of the gradient of a line.
	g2	Know the relationship between the gradients of parallel and perpendicular lines.
	g3	Be able to calculate the distance between two points.
	g4	Be able to find the midpoint of a line segment.
	g5	Be able to form the equation of a straight line.
	g6	Be able to draw a straight line given its equation.
	g7	Be able to solve simultaneous equations graphically.

Student's Book pages 73–96

A straight line can be uniquely defined by two pieces of information, either the co-ordinates of two points or the co-ordinates of one point and the gradient.

The gradient of a line

The gradient of the line joining the two points (x_1, y_1) and (x_2, y_2) is $m = \dfrac{y_2 - y_1}{x_2 - x_1}$.

Example: Find the gradient of the line joining $(1, 2)$ to $(6, 8)$.

Answer: Gradient $= \dfrac{8 - 2}{6 - 1} = \dfrac{6}{5}$

Parallel and perpendicular lines

Parallel lines have the same gradient.

Example: You are given the four points A $(2, 3)$, B $(5, 7)$, C $(6, 0)$, and D $(12, 8)$.
Show that AB and CD are parallel.

Answer: Gradient of AB $= \dfrac{7 - 3}{5 - 2} = \dfrac{4}{3}$

Gradient of CD $= \dfrac{8 - 0}{12 - 6} = \dfrac{8}{6}$

Since these are equal the lines are parallel.

Perpendicular lines are lines with gradients m_1 and m_2 such that $m_1 \times m_2 = -1$.

Example: For A, B and C in the example above, show that AB and AC are perpendicular.

Answer: Gradient of AB $= \dfrac{7 - 3}{5 - 2} = \dfrac{4}{3}$

Gradient of AC $= \dfrac{0 - 3}{6 - 2} = -\dfrac{3}{4}$

Since $\dfrac{4}{3} \times -\dfrac{3}{4} = -1$, the lines AB and AC are perpendicular.

The distance between two points

You can use Pythagoras' theorem to calculate the distance between two points.

The distance between the two points (x_1, y_1) and (x_2, y_2) is $d = \sqrt{(y_2 - y_1)^2 + (x_2 - x_1)^2}$.

Example: Find the distance between the points $(-1, -3)$ and $(3, 4)$.

Answer:
$$d = \sqrt{(4 - -3)^2 + (3 - -1)^2}$$
$$= \sqrt{49 + 16}$$
$$= \sqrt{65}$$

The midpoint of a line joining two points

The midpoint of the line between points (x_1, y_1) and (x_2, y_2) is $M\left(\dfrac{x_1 + x_2}{2}, \dfrac{y_1 + y_2}{2}\right)$.

Example: Find the midpoint of the line AB, where the co-ordinates of A and B are $(3, 5)$ and $(7, 6)$ respectively.

Answer: Midpoint $= \left(\dfrac{3 + 7}{2}, \dfrac{5 + 6}{2}\right) = \left(5, 5\tfrac{1}{2}\right)$

The equation of a line

There are a number of different forms of the equation of a line. The most basic form is $y = mx + c$ but different forms may be more suitable for the situations you will meet.

Example: Find the equation of the line with gradient 2 that passes through the point $(0, -2)$.

Answer: The most convenient form in this case is $y = mx + c$ because c is the intercept on the y-axis.

So $m = 2$ and $c = -2$ $\Rightarrow$ $y = 2x - 2$.

Example: Find the equation of the line with gradient 3 that passes through the point $(1, 4)$.

Answer: The most convenient form in this case is $y - y_1 = m(x - x_1)$.

(x_1, y_1) is $(1, 4)$ and $m = 3$. This gives $y - 4 = 3(x - 1)$.

$$\Rightarrow \quad y - 4 = 3x - 3$$
$$\Rightarrow \quad y = 3x + 1$$

Example: Find the equation of the line through $(2, 3)$ and $(7, 10)$.

Answer: The most convenient form in this case is $\dfrac{y - y_1}{y_2 - y_1} = \dfrac{x - x_1}{x_2 - x_1}$.

(x_1, y_1) is $(2, 3)$ and (x_2, y_2) is $(7, 10)$. This gives $\dfrac{y - 3}{10 - 3} = \dfrac{x - 2}{7 - 2}$.

$$\Rightarrow \quad \frac{y - 3}{7} = \frac{x - 2}{5}$$
$$\Rightarrow \quad 5y - 15 = 7x - 14$$
$$\Rightarrow \quad 5y = 7x + 1$$

⚠ You should multiply out and simplify any equations of lines. For instance, neither $y - 2 = 3(x - 1)$ nor $y - 2 = 3x - 3$ would be acceptable as a final answer. These should be simplified to $y = 3x - 1$.

Solving simultaneous equations graphically

'Simultaneous equations' are equations that are satisfied at the same time. Two lines intersect at one point and so two linear equations are solved simultaneously to give one co-ordinate pair.

The algebraic solution of two linear equations has been covered in Section 1. A solution may also be found graphically by drawing the lines on graph paper and seeing where they intersect.

Example: Solve simultaneously:

$$2x + 3y = 11 \qquad \text{①}$$
$$7x - y = 4 \qquad \text{②}$$

Answer: Draw the straight line graphs of the two equations.
It can be seen that they intersect at $(1, 3)$.

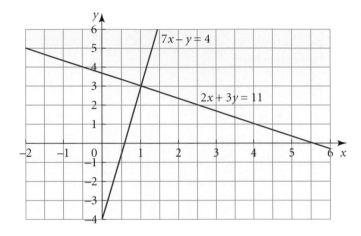

(For the algebraic solution, see the examples on page 6.)

⭐ ■ The most usual forms of an equation for a straight line are as follows.

$$y = mx + c \qquad y - y_1 = m(x - x_1) \qquad \frac{y - y_1}{y_2 - y_1} = \frac{x - x_1}{x_2 - x_1}$$

■ Parallel lines have equal gradients.
■ Perpendicular lines have gradients m_1 and m_2 such that $m_1 \times m_2 = -1$.

Exercise 2.1

1 Write down the gradients of the following lines.

   (i) $y = 2x + 1$ **(ii)** $2y = x + 1$ **(iii)** $3y + 2x = 4$

2 **(i)** Find the equation of the line parallel to $x + 2y = 3$ that passes through the point $(4, 6)$.

   (ii) Find the equation of the line perpendicular to $x + 2y = 3$ that passes through the point $(4, 6)$.

3 You are given the co-ordinates of the four points A $(1, 2)$, B $(4, 6)$, C $(8, 3)$ and D $(5, -1)$. Show that ABCD is a rectangle.

4 Points A and B have co-ordinates $(1, 3)$ and $(7, 5)$.

   (i) Find the midpoint of AB.

   (ii) Find the distance between the points A and B.

5 Find the equations of the following lines.

   (i) Through the points $(-1, -3)$ and $(4, 2)$.

   (ii) Through $(4, 3)$ with gradient -3.

6 By drawing the lines of the two equations, solve graphically the simultaneous equations $3x + 5y = 14$ and $y = 2x - 5$.

2 Circles

The co-ordinate geometry of circles	g8	Know that the equation of a circle, centre (0, 0), radius r, is $x^2 + y^2 = r^2$.
	g9	Know that $(x - a)^2 + (y - b)^2 = r^2$ is the equation of a circle with centre (a, b) and radius r.

Student's Book pages 96–100

The definition of a circle is that it is all the points that are a given distance from a fixed point. The fixed point is the centre and the given distance is the radius.

The equation of a circle with centre at the origin

By Pythagoras' theorem, all points (x, y) have distance r from O $(0, 0)$ where $(x - 0)^2 + (y - 0)^2 = r^2$. This gives $x^2 + y^2 = r^2$, which is the equation of the circle.

> **Example:** Find the equation of a circle with centre at the origin and radius 4.
>
> **Answer:** $x^2 + y^2 = r^2$ with $r = 4$ $\Rightarrow$ $x^2 + y^2 = 16$

The equation of a circle with centre at (*a*, *b*)

By Pythagoras' theorem, all points (x, y) have distance r from (a, b) where $(x - a)^2 + (y - b)^2 = r^2$, which is the equation of the circle.

> **Example:** Find the equation of the circle with centre (2, 3) and radius 5.
>
> **Answer:** $(x - a)^2 + (y - b)^2 = r^2$ with $r = 5$ and $(a, b) = (2, 3)$
>
> $\Rightarrow$ $(x - 2)^2 + (y - 3)^2 = 25$

The brackets may be expanded to give a general equation.

$$x^2 - 2ax + a^2 + y^2 - 2by + b^2 = r^2$$
$$\Rightarrow x^2 + y^2 - 2ax - 2by + a^2 + b^2 - r^2 = 0$$

This equation therefore represents a circle whose centre and radius can be determined from the coefficients by completing the square.

> **Example:** Find the centre and radius of the circle $x^2 + y^2 - 2x + 4y - 4 = 0$.
>
> **Answer:**
> $$x^2 + y^2 - 2x + 4y - 4 = 0$$
> $$\Rightarrow x^2 - 2x + y^2 + 4y - 4 = 0$$
> $$\Rightarrow \left(x^2 - 2x + 1\right) + \left(y^2 + 4y + 4\right) - 4 = 1 + 4 = 5$$
> $$\Rightarrow \left(x - 1\right)^2 + \left(y + 2\right)^2 = 9$$
>
> This represents a circle with a centre at $(1, -2)$ and radius $\sqrt{9} = 3$.

⭐
- The equation of a circle with centre the origin and radius r is $x^2 + y^2 = r^2$.
- The equation of a circle with centre (a, b) and radius r is $(x - a)^2 + (y - b)^2 = r^2$.
- When expanded this becomes $x^2 + y^2 - 2ax - 2by + c = 0$ where $c = a^2 + b^2 - r^2$.

Exercise 2.2

1 Write down the equation of a circle with centre the origin and radius 3.

2 Write down the equation of a circle with centre (2, 1) and radius 3.

3 Show that the equation below represents a circle and find the centre and radius.

$$x^2 + y^2 + 6x - 4y - 8 = 0$$

4 Determine whether the point A(2, 3) lies inside or outside the circle with equation

$$(x - 3)^2 + (y - 1)^2 = 4.$$

Linear programming

Inequalities	g10	Be able to illustrate linear inequalities in two variables.
Applications to linear programming	g11	Be able to express real situations in terms of linear inequalities.
	g12	Be able to use graphs of linear inequalities to solve 2-dimensional maximisation and minimisation problems, know the definition of objective function and be able to find it in 2-dimensional cases.

Student's Book pages 101–117

Inequalities in two variables can be illustrated graphically by the region of points that lie on one side of a line. This is extended to finding a region of points that satisfy a number of inequalities. Finally, we look to maximise or minimise a linear function of the two variables within this region.

Linear inequalities in two variables

A linear inequality in two variables takes the form $ax + by < c$ with the inequality sign $<, >, \geqslant$ or $\leqslant$.

The equality $ax + by = c$ forms the boundary line for the inequality $ax + by < c$, and the acceptable region of points is one side of the line. To find out which side, choose any point at random (e.g. the origin) and test it in the inequality.

Conventions

It is usual to adopt the following conventions.

- The area that is **not** wanted is shaded.
- If the line is included in the acceptable region (i.e. the inequality is $\geqslant$ or $\leqslant$), then the line is drawn solid. If it is not included (i.e. the inequality is $<$ or $>$) then the line is drawn broken.

Example: Illustrate the region satisfying the inequality $2x + 3y \leqslant 12$.

Answer: The line $2x + 3y = 12$ goes through the points $(6, 0)$ and $(0, 4)$.
By substitution, the origin $(0, 0)$ satisfies the inequality and so the acceptable region is the side of the line on which $(0, 0)$ lies. Because the sign is $\leqslant$, the points on the line are included and the line is drawn solid.

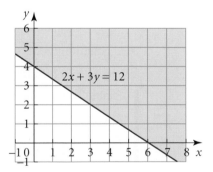

Example: Illustrate the region satisfying the inequality $x + 4y > 12$.

Answer: The line $x + 4y = 12$ goes through the points $(12, 0)$ and $(0, 3)$.
The origin does not satisfy the inequality and so the acceptable region is the other side of the line from which $(0, 0)$ lies. Because the sign is $>$, the points on the line are not included and the line is drawn broken.

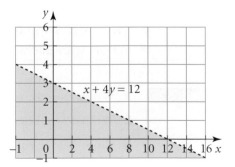

Definition 1

The area that is wanted is called the **feasible region**.

Example: Illustrate the feasible region for the following inequalities.

$$3 \leqslant x \leqslant 6$$
$$y \geqslant 0$$
$$4x + 5y \leqslant 40$$

Answer: The feasible region is the unshaded area.

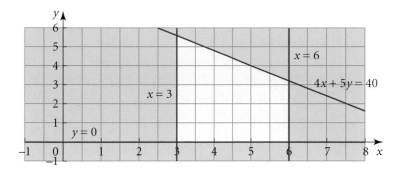

Definition 2

A function to be maximised or minimised in the feasible region is called the **objective function**.

Example: (i) Illustrate the feasible region for the following inequalities.

$$y > x$$
$$x \geqslant 1$$
$$2x + 3y \leqslant 20$$

(ii) Within this region, maximise the function $P = 2x + 5y$.

Answer: (i) The feasible region is illustrated on the graph.

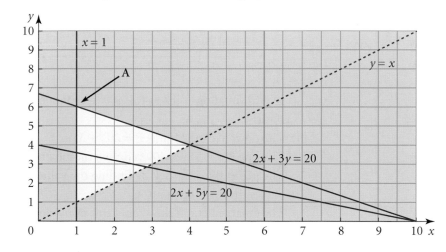

(ii) The line $2x + 5y = 20$ is shown on the graph. There are points on this line within the feasible region. The problem is to find the maximum value of k where $2x + 5y = k$. So we need to find the line through a vertex of the region. In this case it can be seen that this will be at A, which is (1, 6), and so $2x + 5y = 32$.

Maximising the objective function

If $P = ax + by$ then draw the line with P at any arbitrary value. It can then be seen which of the vertices will give the maximum value for P.

If the problem is set in context then it is most likely that there is a restriction that x and y must be integers. If the required vertex does not have integer co-ordinates then points close to the vertex much be chosen and tested, with the greatest value chosen.

Example: The cost of the raw materials plus labour needed to make a chair is £45. For a table the cost is £50. A furniture maker can only outlay £700 per day. He must make at least three times as many chairs as tables.
(i) Illustrate these inequalities on a graph.
(ii) The profit on a chair is £20 and for a table it is £35. Find the number of chairs and tables that should be made, assuming that they will all be sold, to maximise the profit.

Answer: (i) Let x be the number of chairs made and y be the number of tables made. Then the inequalities are

$$45x + 50y \leqslant 700$$
$$x \geqslant 3y$$

The graph is as shown.

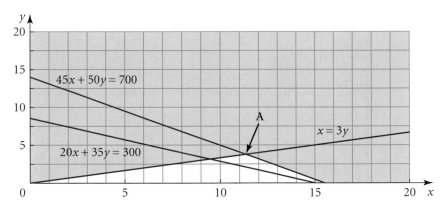

In real situations such as this it is acceptable to assume that both x and y are positive.

(ii) The objective function is $P = 20x + 35y$.
The line $20x + 35y = 300$ is drawn on the graph above.
The profit is maximised by finding the value of P so that the line $P = 20x + 35y$ passes through the point A.
The enlarged graph shows that this point does not have integer co-ordinates.

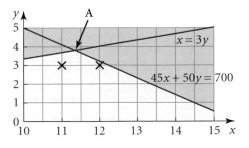

The nearest points are $(11, 3)$ and $(12, 3)$.
So the manufacturer should make 12 chairs and 3 tables, giving a profit of $12 \times £20 + 3 \times £35 = £345$.

★ ■ When illustrating linear inequalities:
  ● indicate the region wanted by shading the **other** side of the line
  ● represent $\leqslant$ and $\geqslant$ with a solid line
  ● represent $<$ and $>$ with a broken line.
■ The **feasible region** is the region that is satisfied by a number of inequalities and is the region on your graph that is **not** shaded.
■ The **objective function** is the function that is to be maximised or minimised.

Exercise 2.3

1 Illustrate the feasible region for the following inequalities.

$$x \geqslant 0$$
$$y \geqslant 0$$
$$y < x$$
$$x + y \leqslant 10$$

2 (i) Illustrate the feasible region for the following inequalities.

$$x \geqslant 0$$
$$y \geqslant 0$$
$$5x + y \leqslant 24$$
$$2x + 3y \leqslant 20$$

(ii) Maximise $P = 4x + y$ in this region.

3 (i) Illustrate the feasible region for the following inequalities.

$$y \geqslant x$$
$$4x + 3y \geqslant 27$$

(ii) Minimise $P = 3x + 5y$ in this region for integer values of (x, y).

4 On a school trip, 120 students and staff need to be transported by coach or minibus.
Each minibus can hold 12 people and each coach can hold 30 people.
There are only 8 drivers available.
Let the number of minibuses used be x and the number of coaches used be y.
Form two inequalities in x and y from the information given.
Draw the inequalities on a graph.
Assuming that $x \geqslant 0$, find

  (i) the combination of vehicles that uses all 8 drivers with the minimum number of spare seats

  (ii) the combination of vehicles which minimises the number of drivers and will carry all 120 people.

1 The vertices of a quadrilateral are A $(-2, 0)$, B $(2, 2)$, C $(7, -3)$ and D $(0, -4)$.

    (i) Calculate the gradients of the diagonals AC and BD and state a geometrical fact about these lines. [3]

    (ii) Show that the midpoint of BD lies on AC. [3]

                                                                [OCR 2004 Q1]

2 (i) Show that the two lines whose equations are given below are parallel.

$$y = 4 - 2x \qquad\qquad 4x + 2y = 5$$

                                                                    [2]

    (ii) Find the equation of the line which is perpendicular to these two lines and which passes through the point $(1, 6)$. [3]

                                                                [OCR 2006 Q7]

3 (i) A circle has equation $x^2 + y^2 - 2x - 4y - 20 = 0$. Find the co-ordinates of its centre, C, and its radius. [3]

    (ii) Find the co-ordinates of the points A and B, where the line $y = x + 2$ cuts the circle. [5]

    (iii) Find the angle ACB. [4]

                                                                 [OCR 2005 Q12]

4 (i) By drawing suitable graphs on the same axes, indicate the region for which the following inequalities hold. You should shade the region which is **not** required. [5]

$$3x + 4y \leqslant 24$$
$$3x + y \leqslant 15$$
$$x \geqslant 0$$
$$y \geqslant 0$$

    (ii) Find the maximum value of $2x + y$ subject to these conditions. [2]

                                                                    [OCR 2003 Q5]

5 A small factory makes two types of components, X and Y. Each component of type X requires materials costing £18 and each component of type Y requires materials costing £11. In each week materials worth £200 are available.

Each component of type X takes 7 man hours to finish and each component of type Y takes 6 man hours to finish. There are 84 man hours available each week.

Components cannot be left part-finished at the end of the week. In addition, in order to satisfy customer demands, at least two of each type are to be made each week.

    (i) The factory produces x components of type X and y components of type Y each week. Write down four inequalities for x and y. [4]

    (ii) On a graph draw suitable lines and shade the region that the inequalities do not allow. (Take $1\,\text{cm} = 1$ component on each axis.) [5]

    (iii) If all components made are sold, and the profit on each component of type X is £70 and on each component of type Y is £50, find from your graph the optimal number of each that should be made and the total profit per week. [3]

                                                                    [OCR 2005 Q11]

SECTION 3
Trigonometry

The ratios of the sides of a right-angled triangle form the basis of this topic. This is extended into developing methods for solving triangles with no right angle, 3-dimensional work and angles that are more than 90°.

The trigonometrical ratios

Ratios of any angles and their graphs	t1	Be able to use the definitions of $\sin\theta$, $\cos\theta$ and $\tan\theta$ for any angle (measured in degrees only).
	t2	Be able to apply trigonometry to right-angled triangles.

Student's Book pages 121–131

Conventions

The three sides of a triangle are conventionally labelled as a, b and c and the angles as A, B and C, with A opposite a, etc. Sometimes the angle is labelled A and sometimes it is the vertex that is labelled A. This convention will be used throughout this guide and is used in the exams.

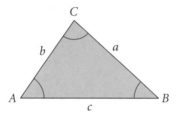

Trigonometrical ratios in right-angled triangles

$$\sin\theta = \frac{\text{opposite}}{\text{hypotenuse}} \qquad \cos\theta = \frac{\text{adjacent}}{\text{hypotenuse}} \qquad \tan\theta = \frac{\text{opposite}}{\text{adjacent}}$$

Example: In a right-angled triangle with sides of length 3, 4 and 5 units, find the angles.

Answer: For one angle, $\sin A = \frac{3}{5}$ and for the other $\sin B = \frac{4}{5}$.

$$\Rightarrow \quad A = \sin^{-1}\left(\frac{3}{5}\right) = 36.9°, \quad B = \sin^{-1}\left(\frac{4}{5}\right) = 53.1°$$

Note that these angles could have been found by using either of the other ratios.

Example: In the triangle ABC, angle C is a right angle, $BC = 2$ units and angle $A = 35°$. Find the lengths of the other two sides of the triangle.

Answer: $\dfrac{2}{AC} = \tan 35° \Rightarrow AC = \dfrac{2}{\tan 35°} = 2.86$ units.

$\dfrac{2}{AB} = \sin 35° \Rightarrow AB = \dfrac{2}{\sin 35°} = 3.49$ units.

Trigonometrical ratios for angles of any size

If a point in the co-ordinate system has co-ordinates (x, y) and is a distance r from the origin then the ratios are defined as follows:

$$\sin\theta = \frac{y}{r} \qquad \cos\theta = \frac{x}{r} \qquad \tan\theta = \frac{y}{x}$$

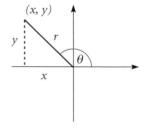

This is consistent with the definitions for a right-angled triangle in that the definitions hold for the first quadrant. These definitions give the ratio for any angle. Note that this means that for any value for a ratio there could be two angles in the range $0° \leqslant \theta \leqslant 360°$.

One way to remember in which quadrants ratios are positive and negative is the mnemonic **CAST**.

In the first quadrant **A**ll three ratios are positive.
In the second quadrant (angles 90°–180°) the **S**ine of an angle is positive, the others being negative, and so on.

S	A
T	C

| Example: $\cos 100° = -0.174$, $\sin 100° = 0.985$, $\tan 100° = -5.671$

Principal Angles

When you use your calculator to find an angle, only one angle can be shown. As described above, however, there are two angles in the range $0° \leqslant \theta \leqslant 360°$. The angle shown on your calculator is called the Principal Angle and the other one has to be worked out.

There are two ranges used by different calculators to give the Principal Angle. One is $0° \leqslant \theta \leqslant 360°$ and the other is $-180° \leqslant \theta \leqslant 180°$.

Example: If $\cos\theta = 0.4$ then find θ in the range $0° \leqslant \theta \leqslant 360°$.

Answer: The Principal Angle is $\theta = 66.4°$.
The other angle is in the fourth quadrant and so is

$$\theta = 360° - 66.4° = 293.6°.$$

Example: Find the two values of θ that satisfy $\tan\theta = -0.3$ in the range $0° \leqslant \theta \leqslant 360°$.

Answer: If your calculator gives the Principal Angle in the range $-180° \leqslant \theta \leqslant 180°$ then $\theta = -16.7°$.
The tangent ratio is negative in the second and fourth quadrants so the two values are $360° - 16.7° = 343.3°$ and $180° - 16.7° = 163.3°$.

If you are asked to solve an equation involving a multiple of θ, make sure you have found all the angles.

Example: Find the four values of θ that satisfy $\sin 2\theta = 0.4$ in the range $0° \leqslant \theta \leqslant 360°$.

Answer: The Principal Angle is $2\theta = 23.6°$.
The other angle is in the second quadrant and so is

$$2\theta = 180° - 23.6° = 156.4°.$$

The period of $\sin x$ is $360°$, so we also need $2\theta = 23.6° + 360° = 383.6°$ and $2\theta = 156.4° + 360° = 516.4°$.
So the four values of θ are $11.8°$, $78.2°$, $191.8°$ and $258.2°$.

⚠ Make sure that you know what range your calculator uses for the Principal Angle.

✪
- The mnemonic **CAST** gives the quadrants in which the given ratio is positive.
- Find out the range used by your calculator.
- If the angle in the first quadrant is θ then the equivalent angles in the second, third and fourth quadrants are $180° - \theta$, $180° + \theta$ and $360° - \theta$.

Exercise 3.1

1 You are given that $\theta = 148°$. Find $\tan\theta$, $\sin\theta$ and $\cos\theta$.

2 Solve the equation $\sin\theta = 0.7$ in the range $0° \leqslant \theta \leqslant 360°$.

3 Solve the equation $\tan\theta = -1.2$ in the range $0° \leqslant \theta \leqslant 360°$.

4 Solve the equation $\cos 2\theta = 0.7$ in the range $0° \leqslant \theta \leqslant 360°$.

2 Identities and equations

Ratios of any angles and their graphs	t5	Know and be able to use the identity $\tan\theta = \dfrac{\sin\theta}{\cos\theta}$
	t6	Know and be able to use the identity $\sin^2\theta + \cos^2\theta = 1$.
	t7	Be able to solve simple trigonometrical equations in given intervals.

Student's Book pages 131–139

Identities

You need to know two identities:

$$\tan\theta = \frac{\sin\theta}{\cos\theta} \qquad \sin^2\theta + \cos^2\theta = 1$$

These are true for all angles, θ.

Example: You are given that $\sin\theta = \frac{2}{3}$. Find the exact value of $\cos\theta$.

Answer: $\sin\theta = \frac{2}{3} \quad\Rightarrow\quad \sin^2\theta = \frac{4}{9}$.

Using $\sin^2\theta + \cos^2\theta = 1$ gives $\frac{4}{9} + \cos^2\theta = 1$

$\Rightarrow \quad \cos^2\theta = 1 - \frac{4}{9} = \frac{5}{9}$

$\Rightarrow \quad \cos\theta = \sqrt{\frac{5}{9}} = \frac{1}{3}\sqrt{5}$

Example: (i) Using Pythagoras' theorem on the triangle shown, show that $\sin^2\theta + \cos^2\theta = 1$.

(ii) Hence, given that $\sin\theta = \frac{3}{7}$, find the exact value of $\tan\theta$.

Answer: (i) $a^2 + b^2 = c^2$

$\Rightarrow \qquad \dfrac{a^2}{c^2} + \dfrac{b^2}{c^2} = \dfrac{c^2}{c^2}$

$\Rightarrow \qquad \left(\dfrac{a}{c}\right)^2 + \left(\dfrac{b}{c}\right)^2 = 1$

$\Rightarrow \quad \sin^2\theta + \cos^2\theta = 1$

(ii) $\sin\theta = \frac{3}{7} \quad\Rightarrow\quad \sin^2\theta = \frac{9}{49}$

$\Rightarrow \quad \cos^2\theta = 1 - \frac{9}{49} = \frac{40}{49}$

$\Rightarrow \quad \cos\theta = \sqrt{\frac{40}{49}} = \frac{1}{7}\sqrt{40} = \frac{1}{7}\sqrt{4 \times 10} = \frac{2}{7}\sqrt{10}$

$\Rightarrow \quad \tan\theta = \dfrac{\sin\theta}{\cos\theta} = \dfrac{\frac{3}{7}}{\frac{2}{7}\sqrt{10}} = \dfrac{3}{2\sqrt{10}} = \dfrac{3}{2\sqrt{10}} \times \dfrac{\sqrt{10}}{\sqrt{10}} = \dfrac{3\sqrt{10}}{20}$

⚠ ■ The identities are **not** given on the formula sheet of the exam paper and so need to be learned.
■ If the question asks for an **exact** value then you should **not** use your calculator to find the angle. Finding θ and then $\cos\theta$ using your calculator will not give an exact value and will earn no marks in the exam.

 Always take out a perfect square from a square root.

Solving equations

Equations involving the trigonometrical ratios are solved in a variety of ways, using the identities above. In the exam the range will always be $0° \leqslant \theta \leqslant 360°$. Sometimes there will be two solutions that need to be found but sometimes there will be four solutions.

Example: Solve the equation $3\cos\theta + 2 = 0$ in the range $0° \leqslant \theta \leqslant 360°$.

Answer: $3\cos\theta + 2 = 0$

$$\Rightarrow \quad \cos\theta = -\frac{2}{3}$$

$$\Rightarrow \quad \theta = 131.8°$$

The other angle is $360° - 131.8° = 228.2°$.

Example: Solve the equation $\sin\theta = 2\cos\theta$ in the range $0° \leqslant \theta \leqslant 360°$.

Answer: $\sin\theta = 2\cos\theta$

$$\Rightarrow \quad \frac{\sin\theta}{\cos\theta} = 2$$

$$\Rightarrow \quad \tan\theta = 2$$

$$\Rightarrow \quad \theta = 63.4°$$

The other angle is $180° + 63.4° = 243.4°$.

Example: Solve the equation $3\sin^2\theta + \sin\theta - 1 = 0$ in the range $0° \leqslant \theta \leqslant 360°$.

Answer: Using the formula to find the roots of a quadratic equation gives

$$\sin\theta = \frac{-1 \pm \sqrt{1 + 12}}{6}$$

$$= \frac{-1 \pm \sqrt{13}}{6}$$

$$= -0.7676 \text{ or } 0.4343$$

$$\Rightarrow \quad \theta = -50.1° \text{ or } \theta = 25.7°$$

The first value gives the two solutions $180° + 50.1° = 230.1°$ and $360° - 50.1° = 309.9°$.
The second value gives the two solutions $25.7°$ and $180° - 25.7° = 154.3°$.
The solutions are $\theta = 25.7°$, $\theta = 154.3°$, $\theta = 230.1°$ and $\theta = 309.9°$.

Example: Show that the equation $2\cos^2\theta = 3\sin\theta$ can be written $2\sin^2\theta + 3\sin\theta - 2 = 0$.
Hence solve the equation $2\cos^2\theta = 3\sin\theta$ in the range $0° \leqslant \theta \leqslant 360°$.

Answer:
$$2\cos^2\theta = 3\sin\theta$$

$$\Rightarrow \quad 2(1 - \sin^2\theta) = 3\sin\theta$$

$$\Rightarrow \quad 2 - 2\sin^2\theta = 3\sin\theta$$

$$\Rightarrow \quad 2\sin^2\theta + 3\sin\theta - 2 = 0$$

$$\Rightarrow \quad (\sin\theta + 2)(2\sin\theta - 1) = 0$$

$$\Rightarrow \quad \sin\theta = -2 \text{ or } \sin\theta = \frac{1}{2}$$

The first value is not possible. The second value gives $\theta = \sin^{-1}\left(\frac{1}{2}\right)$.
The solutions are $\theta = 30°$ and $\theta = 150°$.

⭐ ■ Make sure that your solution to a trigonometrical equation includes **all** the angles that satisfy the equation.

■ The identity $\sin^2\theta + \cos^2\theta = 1$ can be rearranged to give $\cos^2\theta = 1 - \sin^2\theta$ and $\sin^2\theta = 1 - \cos^2\theta$.

Exercise 3.2

1 Given that $\cos\theta = \frac{2}{5}$, find the exact value of $\sin\theta$.

2 Solve the equation $4\sin\theta = 7\cos\theta$ for all values of θ in the range $0° \leqslant \theta \leqslant 360°$.

3 Solve the equation $3\cos^2\theta = 2 + \sin\theta$ for all values of θ in the range $0° \leqslant \theta \leqslant 360°$.

3 Area and the sine and cosine rules

Ratios of any angles and their graphs.	t3	Know the sine and cosine rules and be able to apply them.
	t4	Be able to apply trigonometry to triangles with any angles.

Student's Book pages 140–154

This section is about finding angles and the lengths of sides in triangles without a right angle. Where there is a right angle the more basic principles should be used. Be aware that a diagram may look as though the triangle contains a right angle, but if it does not say this then it probably does not.

Area

The area of a triangle is 'half the base times the height'.

From the diagram it can be seen that $h = b \sin C$.

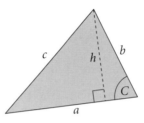

Therefore area $= \frac{1}{2}ah = \frac{1}{2}ab\sin C$.

> **Example:** In a triangle you are given that angle $A = 50°$, $b = 6$ cm and $c = 8$ cm. Find the area of the triangle.
>
> **Answer:** There are two other forms for the area of a triangle, given by rotating the letters. Therefore in this case area $= \frac{1}{2}bc\sin A$
>
> $$\Rightarrow \quad \text{area} = \frac{1}{2} \times 6 \times 8 \times \sin 50°$$
> $$= 24\sin 50°$$
> $$= 18.4 \text{ cm}^2.$$

The sine rule

In any triangle ABC with sides a, b and c,

$$\frac{a}{\sin A} = \frac{b}{\sin B} = \frac{c}{\sin C}.$$

This can be re-written as

$$\frac{\sin A}{a} = \frac{\sin B}{b} = \frac{\sin C}{c}.$$

If three values in one of the equations are known then the fourth can be found.

> **Example:** In a triangle ABC, $a = 5$, $A = 56°$ and $B = 47°$. Find b.
>
> **Answer:** Using the formula $\dfrac{a}{\sin A} = \dfrac{b}{\sin B}$,
>
> $$\frac{5}{\sin 56°} = \frac{b}{\sin 47°}$$
>
> $$\Rightarrow \quad b = \frac{5\sin 47°}{\sin 56°} = 4.41 \text{ units.}$$

The cosine rule

In any triangle ABC with sides a, b and c,

$$a^2 = b^2 + c^2 - 2bc\cos A$$

This can be re-written in two other ways:

$$b^2 = c^2 + a^2 - 2ca\cos B \qquad \text{and} \qquad c^2 = a^2 + b^2 - 2ab\cos C.$$

The cosine can also be made the subject of the formula:

$$\cos A = \frac{b^2 + c^2 - a^2}{2bc}$$

Example: In a triangle ABC, $A = 37°$, $b = 4$ and $c = 6$. Find a.

Answer: $a^2 = b^2 + c^2 - 2bc\cos A$

$\qquad = 4^2 + 6^2 - 2 \times 4 \times 6\cos 37°$

$\qquad = 13.67$

$\Rightarrow \quad a = 3.70 \text{ units.}$

Example: The three sides of a triangle are 6, 7 and 8. Find the size of the largest angle.

Answer: The largest angle is opposite the longest side, which is 8.

Therefore $\cos A = \dfrac{6^2 + 7^2 - 8^2}{2 \times 6 \times 7}$

$\qquad\qquad = 0.25$

$\Rightarrow \quad A = 75.5°$

- The formula for the area of a triangle is area $= \frac{1}{2}ab\sin C$. It is **not** given on the formula sheet.

- The sine rule is $\dfrac{a}{\sin A} = \dfrac{b}{\sin B} = \dfrac{c}{\sin C}$ or $\dfrac{\sin A}{a} = \dfrac{\sin B}{b} = \dfrac{\sin C}{c}$. This formula is **not** given on the formula sheet.

- The cosine rule is $a^2 = b^2 + c^2 - 2bc\cos A$. This formula is given on the formula sheet.

- The cosine rule can be written as $\cos A = \dfrac{b^2 + c^2 - a^2}{2bc}$.

Exercise 3.3

1 In the triangle ABC, $b = 6$, $c = 8$ and $A = 47°$. Find the side a. Find also the area of the triangle.

2 In the triangle PQR, $P = 36°$, $QR = 4$ and $PR = 3.5$. Find the angle Q.

3 In the triangle ABC, $a = 6$, $b = 8$ and $c = 11$. Find the sizes of the three angles.

2-D and 3-D problems

Ratios of any angles and their graphs	t8	Be able to apply trigonometry to 2- and 3-dimensional problems.

Student's Book pages 155–165

2-dimensional problems can be drawn on a flat surface. 3-dimensional problems should always be broken down into 2-dimensional figures. Look for, and draw, triangles that can be solved.

The angle between a line and a plane

A line will meet a plane at a single point (unless they are parallel). Call this point A. From another point on the line, B, draw a line to the plane to meet it at a point C in such a way that every line in the plane is perpendicular to it. Then the triangle ABC is right-angled and the angle between the line and the plane is angle A.

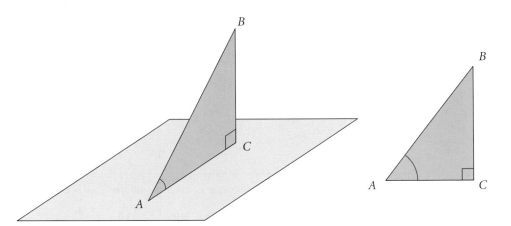

Example: A cuboid is such that all six faces are rectangles.

The horizontal base, $ABCD$, has sides $AB = 5$ cm and $BC = 4$ cm.

The top $EFGH$ is such that E is vertically above A, with $AE = 3$ cm, as shown in the diagram. Find the angle that the diagonal AG makes

(i) with the base $ABCD$

(ii) with the face $ABFE$.

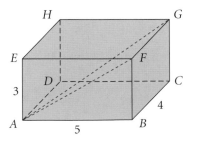

Answer: (i) The triangle we require is ACG with a right angle at C. The required angle is GAC.
In this triangle, $AC^2 = 4^2 + 5^2 = 41$ and $CG = 3$.

$$\text{So } \tan\theta = \frac{3}{\sqrt{41}}$$

$$\Rightarrow \quad \theta = 25.1°$$

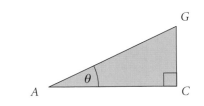

(ii) The triangle we require is *AFG* with a right angle at *F*.
The required angle is *GAF*.
In this triangle $AF^2 = 5^2 + 3^2 = 34$.

So $\tan\phi = \dfrac{4}{\sqrt{34}}$

$\Rightarrow \quad \phi = 34.4°$

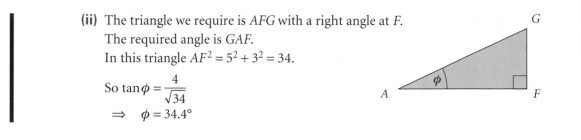

Angle of greatest slope

Two planes meet in a line. From any point, *A*, on the line, draw a line in each plane that is perpendicular to the common line. The angle between these two lines is the angle between the planes. This is the angle of greatest slope.

From a common point on the line, draw a line in each plane that is perpendicular to the common line. The angle between these two lines is the angle between the planes.

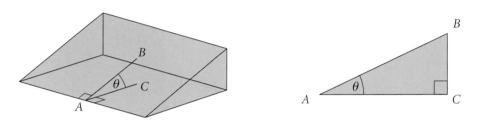

Example: In the example above, the plane *ADGF* meets the base in the line *AD*. What is the angle of greatest slope?

Answer: The angle is *FAB = GDC*.

So angle $FAB = \tan^{-1}\left(\dfrac{3}{5}\right) = 31.0°$

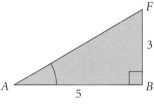

⭐ Draw right-angled triangles in two dimensions as often as possible.

Exercise 3.4   In the diagram shown, *ABCD* is a horizontal rectangle and *CDFE* is a vertical rectangle.

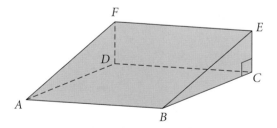

$AB = DC = FE = 10\,\text{cm}$. $BC = AD = 6\,\text{cm}$. $CE = DF = 4\,\text{cm}$.

1 Find the following angles.

(i) *EBC*

(ii) *EAC*

2 Which of these two is the angle of greatest slope?

1 Find the four values of x in the range $0° \leqslant x \leqslant 360°$ that satisfy the equation $\sin 2x = 0.5$. [4]

[OCR 6993 2003]

2 (i) Using the identity $\cos^2\theta + \sin^2\theta = 1$, show that the equation

$$2\cos^2\theta + \sin\theta = 2$$

can be written as

$$2\sin^2\theta - \sin\theta = 0.$$ [2]

(ii) Hence find all values of θ in the range $0° \leqslant \theta \leqslant 180°$ satisfying the equation

$$2\cos^2\theta + \sin\theta = 2.$$ [4]

[OCR 2005 Q10]

3 Calculate the values of x in the range $0° \leqslant x \leqslant 360°$ for which $\sin x = 3\cos x$. [4]

4 Use the given triangle to prove that, for $0° \leqslant \theta \leqslant 90°$, $1 + \tan^2\theta = \dfrac{1}{\cos^2\theta}$. [3]

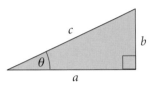

[OCR 6993 2003]

5 A pyramid $ABCDV$ has a square, horizontal base $ABCD$ of side 6 cm. The vertex V is vertically above the centre of the base O. The pyramid has height 7 cm.

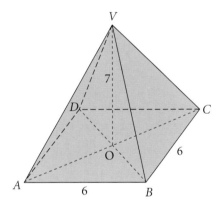

Find the angle that the sloping edge VA makes with the horizontal. [5]

[OCR 6993 2003]

6 (i) Find the value of x in the range $0° \leqslant x \leqslant 360°$ that satisfies **both** $\tan x = 0.75$ **and** $\cos x = -0.8$. [3]

(ii) Find all the values of x in the range $0° \leqslant x \leqslant 360°$ that satisfy $\sin x = -2\cos x$. [3]

[OCR 6993 2004]

SECTION 4
Calculus

This section is about finding rates of change, or gradient functions, which is called differentiation. It also covers the reverse process, called integration. Both processes have applications in finding stationary points and areas, and in kinematics.

1 Differentiation

Differentiation	c1	Be able to differentiate kx^n where n is a positive integer or 0, and the sum of such functions.
	c2	Know that the gradient function $\frac{dy}{dx}$ gives the gradient of the curve and measures the rate of change of y with x.

Student's Book pages 169–177

Differentiation

Differentiating a term is finding the gradient function.

If $y = ax^n$ then the gradient function is $\frac{dy}{dx} = nax^{n-1}$.

> **Example:** Find the gradient function of the function $y = x^3$.
>
> **Answer:** The gradient function is $\frac{dy}{dx} = 3 \times x^{3-1}$
> $= 3x^2$.

Each term of an expression is treated separately.

> **Example:** Find the gradient function of the function $y = x^2 + 3x^4$.
>
> **Answer:** The gradient function is $\frac{dy}{dx} = 2x^{2-1} + 4 \times 3x^{4-1}$
> $= 2x + 12x^3$.

Gradient of a curve

If $y = f(x)$ is the equation of a curve then the gradient function $\frac{dy}{dx}$ gives the gradient at a point on the curve.

> **Example:** Find the gradient of the curve $y = 4x^2 - x^3$ at the point $(2, 8)$.
>
> **Answer:** The gradient is $\frac{dy}{dx} = 8x - 3x^2$.
>
> When $x = 2$, $\frac{dy}{dx} = 16 - 12 = 4$.

⭐ ■ If $y = ax^n$, then $\frac{dy}{dx} = nax^{n-1}$

■ In this specification, n is a positive integer.

■ If $y = c$, then $\frac{dy}{dx} = 0$

■ Terms are differentiated separately when they are added or subtracted. Terms that are multiplied or divided cannot be differentiated using this rule.

Exercise 4.1

1 Differentiate the following functions.

   (i) $y = x^2 + x - 2$

   (ii) $y = 2x^3 + 3x - 5$

2 Find the gradient of the curve $y = x^2 - 4x - 1$ at the point $(2, -5)$.

3 Find the gradient of the curve $y = x(x - 4)$ at the point $(0, 0)$.

Tangents and normals

| Differentiation | c3 | Know that the gradient of the function is the gradient of the tangent at that point. |
| | c4 | Be able to find the equation of a tangent and normal at any point on a curve. |

Student's Book pages 177–182

A tangent to a curve at a point is the line that touches the curve at that point. The gradient of the tangent is the gradient of the curve at that point.

The normal at a point is the line through that point which is perpendicular to the tangent. Perpendicular lines have gradients m_1 and m_2 such that $m_1 \times m_2 = -1$.

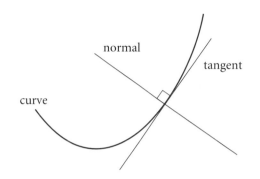

Tangents

To find the equation of the tangent at a point on a curve:

- find the gradient function of the curve, $\dfrac{\mathrm{d}y}{\mathrm{d}x}$
- substitute the value of the x co-ordinate into the gradient function to find the gradient
- use a standard form of the equation of a line with the calculated gradient and through the point on the curve.

Example: Find the equation of the tangent to the curve $y = x^3 - 2x + 3$ at the point $(2, 7)$.

Answer: $y = x^3 - 2x + 3$

$$\Rightarrow \quad \frac{\mathrm{d}y}{\mathrm{d}x} = 3x^2 - 2$$

When $x = 2$, $\dfrac{\mathrm{d}y}{\mathrm{d}x} = 3 \times 4 - 2 = 10$.

The equation of the tangent is $y - y_1 = m(x - x_1)$.

You have just found that the gradient (m) is 10 at the point $(2, 7)$.

Use $x_1 = 2$ and $y_1 = 7$.

$$y - y_1 = m(x - x_1)$$
$$\Rightarrow \quad y - 7 = 10(x - 2)$$
$$\Rightarrow \quad y = 10x - 13$$

Normals

To find the equation of the normal at a point on a curve:

- find the gradient function of the curve

- substitute the value of the x co-ordinate into the gradient function to find the gradient

- use $m_1 \times m_2 = -1$ to find the gradient of the normal

- use a standard form of the equation of a line with the calculated gradient and through the point on the curve.

Example: Find the equation of the normal to the curve $y = x^3 - 3x^2 - 6x + 11$ at the point $(3, -7)$.

Answer: $y = x^3 - 3x^2 - 6x + 11$

$$\Rightarrow \quad \frac{dy}{dx} = 3x^2 - 6x - 6$$

When $x = 3$, $\dfrac{dy}{dx} = 3 \times 9 - 6 \times 3 - 6 = 3$

$$m_1 \times m_2 = -1$$
$$\Rightarrow \quad m_2 = -\frac{1}{m_1} = -\frac{1}{3}$$
$$y - y_1 = m(x - x_1)$$
$$\Rightarrow \quad y + 7 = -\frac{1}{3}(x - 3)$$
$$\Rightarrow \quad 3y + 21 = 3 - x$$
$$\Rightarrow \quad 3y + x + 18 = 0$$

■ Write the equation of a tangent or normal in the form $ax + by + c = 0$. Fractions may be left but there should be only one constant term. For example, it would not have been a complete answer to leave the equation above as $3y + 21 = 3 - x$.

■ If you are asked to find the equation of the normal at a point then you need to find the gradient of the tangent, but you do not need to find the equation of the tangent.

■ The gradient of the tangent at a point on a curve is the value of the gradient function at that point.

■ The normal at that point is perpendicular to the tangent.

Exercise 4.2

1 Find the equation of the tangent to the curve $y = x^3 + x^2 - 3x + 1$ at the point $(2, 7)$.

2 Find the equation of the normal to the curve $y = x^3 - x^2 + 4x - 2$ at the point $(1, 2)$.

3 Find the point on the curve $y = x^2 - 2x + 7$ where the gradient is 8.

4 Find the two points on the curve $y = x^3 - 3x^2 + 6x - 4$ where the gradient is 6.

5 The curve $y = x^2 + 3x + k$ has a tangent with equation $y = 5x + 5$. Find the value of k.

3 Stationary points

Differentiation	c5	Be able to use differentiation to find stationary points on a curve.
	c6	Be able to determine the nature of a stationary point.
	c7	Be able to sketch a curve with known stationary points.

Student's Book pages 182–190

A stationary point on a curve is a point where the gradient is zero. The tangent at this point is parallel to the x-axis and the normal at this point is parallel to the y-axis. Such a point is also called a turning point. At these points, either:

- The gradient changes from having a negative value, through 0, to having a positive value. This is called a minimum point.

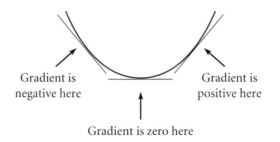

OR

- The gradient changes from having a positive value, through 0, to having a negative value. This is called a maximum point.

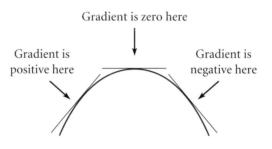

Sketching a curve

The essential details of a curve to be sketched are

- the co-ordinates and nature of any turning points
- the intercepts on the x- and y-axes.

There are three ways to determine whether a turning point is a maximum or a minimum.

1 Use values of the function

Calculate the value of the function at the turning point, and at a point on each side close to the turning point. For instance, if the value at the turning point is greater than at the points on either side, then the turning point is a maximum.

2 Use values of the gradient

Calculate the value of the gradient on each side of the turning point and at the turning point. If the gradients of these three points are negative, 0 and then positive as you move in the positive x direction, then the turning point is a minimum.

3 Use the rate of change of the gradient

If the values of the gradient are negative, 0 and then positive, the gradient function is an increasing function. Therefore its rate of change is positive.

The rate of change of $\dfrac{dy}{dx}$ is denoted by $\dfrac{d^2y}{dx^2}$. If the value of this function is positive, then the gradient is increasing from negative through 0 to positive and so the turning point is a minimum.

The conditions are therefore:

- $\dfrac{d^2y}{dx^2} > 0$ means a minimum point.

- $\dfrac{d^2y}{dx^2} < 0$ means a maximum point.

Example: Investigate the nature of the turning point of the curve $y = 2x^3 - 3x^2 - 12x + 24$ that is in the positive quadrant.

Answer: $y = 2x^3 - 3x^2 - 12x + 24$

$$\Rightarrow \quad \frac{dy}{dx} = 6x^2 - 6x - 12$$

When $\dfrac{dy}{dx} = 0$

$$6x^2 - 6x - 12 = 0$$
$$\Rightarrow \quad x^2 - x - 2 = 0$$
$$\Rightarrow \quad (x - 2)(x + 1) = 0$$

So the turning point in the positive quadrant is when $x = 2$.

$$x = 2 \quad \Rightarrow \quad y = 4$$

Method 1

$f(1.9) = 4.088$

$f(2) = 4$

$f(2.1) = 4.092$ so at $x = 2$ there is a minimum point.

Method 2

$$\frac{dy}{dx} = 6x^2 - 6x - 12$$

When $x = 1.9$, $\frac{dy}{dx} = -1.74$.

When $x = 2$, $\frac{dy}{dx} = 0$.

When $x = 2.1$, $\frac{dy}{dx} = 1.86$.

Since the gradient goes from negative to 0 to positive, the turning point is a minimum.

Method 3

$$\frac{dy}{dx} = 6x^2 - 6x - 12$$

$$\Rightarrow \quad \frac{d^2y}{dx^2} = 12x - 6$$

When $x = 2$, $\frac{d^2y}{dx^2} = 24 - 6 > 0$ so at $x = 2$ there is a minimum point.

Different notations

In the examples above, y is expressed as a function of x. More generally we may write $y = f(x)$.

In this case, $\frac{dy}{dx} = f'(x)$.

You might have a function of different variables. For instance, $A = \pi r^2 \Rightarrow \frac{dA}{dr} = 2\pi r$.

- ■ The three ways to check whether a turning point is a maximum or a minimum are:

  - ● find values of the function at the turning point and close to it on each side

  - ● find values of the gradient at points close to the turning point on each side

  - ● find the value of $\frac{d^2y}{dx^2}$ at the turning point – a positive value means a minimum and a negative value means a maximum.

- ■ Sketching a curve should include the turning points and any intersections with the x- and y-axes.

Exercise 4.3

1 Find the co-ordinates and the nature of the turning points of $y = x^3 - 4x^2 + 5x - 2$. Sketch the curve.

2 The perimeter of a rectangular enclosure is 100 m.

   (i) If one side of the enclosure is x m then show that the area, A m^2, of the enclosure is given by $A = x(50 - x)$.

   (ii) Find the value of x that will give the maximum area.

3 Show that the curve $y = x^3 + x^2 + x + 1$ has no turning point.

Integration

Integration	c8	Be aware that integration is the reverse of differentiation.
	c9	Be able to integrate kx^n where n is a positive integer or 0, and the sum of such functions.
	c10	Be able to find a constant of integration.
	c11	Be able to find the equation of a curve, given its gradient function and one point.

Student's Book pages 191–196

Differentiation reversed

Integration is the reverse of differentiation.

If $\dfrac{dy}{dx} = ax^n$ then $y = \dfrac{ax^{n+1}}{n+1} + c$.

c is called the constant of integration. If you differentiate a constant you get 0, so when you integrate you need to write it in.

In this specification, n is a positive integer or 0.

> **Example:** Integrate $6x^3$.
>
> **Answer:** $6 \times \dfrac{x^4}{4} + c = \dfrac{3x^4}{2} + c$

As with differentiation, terms that are added or subtracted are integrated term by term.

> **Example:** If $\dfrac{dy}{dx} = 4x^2 + x^3 - 5x^4$, find y.
>
> **Answer:** $\dfrac{dy}{dx} = 4x^2 + x^3 - 5x^4$
>
> $\Rightarrow \quad y = 4 \times \dfrac{x^3}{3} + \dfrac{x^4}{4} - 5 \times \dfrac{x^5}{5} + c$
>
> $\Rightarrow \quad y = \dfrac{4x^3}{3} + \dfrac{x^4}{4} - x^5 + c$

Finding a function $y = f(x)$ by integrating a gradient function should include the constant, c. The result is a 'family' of curves, each of which is found by a particular value of c. The equation (such as the one in the example above) is called the **general solution**. Finding a **particular solution** requires an additional piece of information (such as a point through which the curve passes) that determines the value of c.

> **Example:** The gradient function of a curve is given by $\dfrac{dy}{dx} = 3x^2 - 2x + 1$
>
> Find the equation of the curve, given that it passes through the point (1, 2).
>
> **Answer:** $\dfrac{dy}{dx} = 3x^2 - 2x + 1 \quad \Rightarrow \quad y = x^3 - x^2 + x + c$
>
> This equation is satisfied by (1, 2), so substitute $x = 1$, $y = 2$.
>
> $\Rightarrow \quad 2 = 1 - 1 + 1 + c$
>
> $\Rightarrow \quad c = 1$
>
> The equation is $y = x^3 - x^2 + x + 1$.

The integral notation

The process of integrating a function f(x) can be denoted $\int f(x)\,dx$.

Note that this is read 'the integral of f(x) with respect to x', and that the symbol should not be separated from the 'dx'.

Example: Find $\int (6x^2 - 4x)\,dx$.

Answer: $\int (6x^2 - 4x)\,dx = 6 \times \dfrac{x^3}{3} - 4 \times \dfrac{x^2}{2} + c$

$\qquad\qquad\qquad = 2x^3 - 2x^2 + c$

If $\dfrac{dy}{dx} = ax^n$ then $y = \dfrac{ax^{n+1}}{n+1} + c$.

This may also be written $\int ax^n\,dx = \dfrac{ax^{n+1}}{n+1} + c$.

⚠ ■ Do not separate the integral sign from the 'dx'.
■ Do not forget the constant of integration, c.
■ Do not forget to multiply out any brackets before integrating.

✪ ■ If $\dfrac{dy}{dx} = ax^n$ then $y = \int ax^n\,dx = \dfrac{ax^{n+1}}{n+1} + c$.
■ If a particular value of c is required, then substitute for x and y from the given point through which the curve passes.

Exercise 4.4

1 Integrate each of the following.
   (i) x^7
   (ii) $5x^3 + 3x^5$
   (iii) $x(2x - 1)$

2 You are given that $\dfrac{dy}{dx} = x^2 + 2x - 3$. Find y.

3 The gradient function of a curve is given by $\dfrac{dy}{dx} = 2x - 5$. The curve passes through the point $(1, 2)$. Find the equation of the curve.

4 Find each of the following.
   (i) $\int (3x^2 - 4x + 1)\,dx$
   (ii) $\int x(2x - 1)\,dx$
   (iii) $\int (x + 1)(2x - 3)\,dx$

Definite integrals and area

5

Definite integrals	c12	Know what is meant by an indefinite and a definite integral.
	c13	Be able to evaluate definite integrals.
	c14	Be able to find the area between a curve, two ordinates and the x axis.
	c15	Be able to find the area between two curves.

Student's Book pages 196–212

Definite integrals

The integration of a function should include a constant of integration. This gives a 'general' solution. For a particular solution, we use a definite integral. Given two numbers, called the upper and lower limits and written as shown in the example below, you evaluate the function for the upper and the lower limit and subtract. You do not need to involve the constant of integration, c.

Example:
$$\int_2^3 (6x^2 - 4x)\,dx = \left[2x^3 - 2x^2 \right]_2^3$$
$$= \left(2 \times 3^3 - 2 \times 3^2 \right) - \left(2 \times 2^3 - 2 \times 2^2 \right)$$
$$= (54 - 18) - (16 - 8)$$
$$= 36 - 8 = 28$$

Area

The area between a curve $y = f(x)$, the two lines $x = a$ and $x = b$ and the x-axis is $\int_a^b f(x)\,dx$.

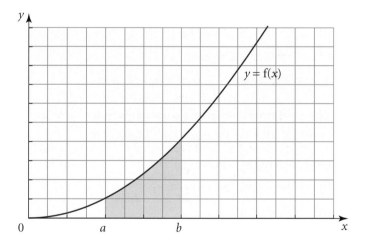

Example: Find the area between the curve $y = 3 + 4x - x^2$, the x-axis and the lines $x = 1$ and $x = 4$.

Answer: Area $= \int_1^4 (3 + 4x - x^2)\,dx$

$$= \left[3x + 2x^2 - \frac{x^3}{3} \right]_1^4$$

$$= \left(3 \times 4 + 2 \times 4^2 - \frac{4^3}{3} \right) - \left(3 + 2 - \frac{1}{3} \right)$$

$$= \left(44 - \frac{64}{3} \right) - \left(5 - \frac{1}{3} \right)$$

$$= 39 - \frac{63}{3}$$

$$= 39 - 21 = 18 \text{ units}^2$$

Example: Find the area between the curve $y = 2x - x^2$ and the x-axis.

Answer: The curve cuts the x-axis at $x = 0$ and $x = 2$.

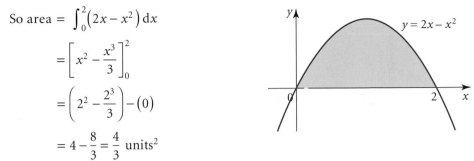

So area $= \displaystyle\int_0^2 \left(2x - x^2\right) dx$

$= \left[x^2 - \dfrac{x^3}{3} \right]_0^2$

$= \left(2^2 - \dfrac{2^3}{3} \right) - (0)$

$= 4 - \dfrac{8}{3} = \dfrac{4}{3}$ units^2

Note that if the curve lies beneath the x-axis then the numerical value of the area will be negative. It follows that if the curve crosses the axis between the limits of x then part will be negative and part positive, giving an incorrect value for the actual area.

Area between two curves

$\text{Area} = \displaystyle\int (\text{top curve})dx - \int (\text{bottom curve})dx$

$= \displaystyle\int (\text{top curve} - \text{bottom curve})dx$

Example: Find the area enclosed by the curve $y = 5 + 2x - x^2$ and the line $x + y = 5$.

Answer: Substitute $y = 5 - x$ to find the intersections with the curve.

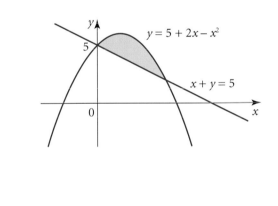

$5 - x = 5 + 2x - x^2$

$\Rightarrow \quad x^2 - 3x = 0$

$\Rightarrow \quad x = 0 \text{ or } x = 3$

$\text{Area} = \displaystyle\int_0^3 \left((5 + 2x - x^2) - (5 - x)\right) dx$

$= \displaystyle\int_0^3 (3x - x^2)dx$

$= \left[\dfrac{3x^2}{2} - \dfrac{x^3}{3} \right]_0^3$

$= \left(\dfrac{27}{2} - \dfrac{27}{3} \right) - 0 = \dfrac{27}{6} = \dfrac{9}{2} \text{units}^2$

Example: Find the area between the curve $y = 13 - 6x + x^2$ and the curve $y = 3 + 6x - x^2$.

Answer: You first need to find where the curves intersect.

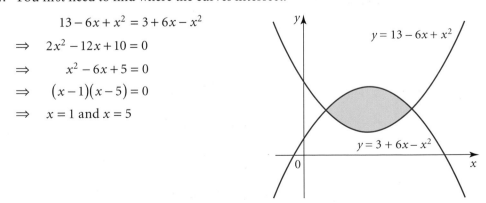

$13 - 6x + x^2 = 3 + 6x - x^2$

$\Rightarrow \quad 2x^2 - 12x + 10 = 0$

$\Rightarrow \quad x^2 - 6x + 5 = 0$

$\Rightarrow \quad (x - 1)(x - 5) = 0$

$\Rightarrow \quad x = 1 \text{ and } x = 5$

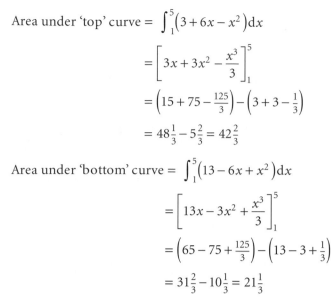

Method 1

Area under 'top' curve $= \int_{1}^{5}\left(3+6x-x^2\right)dx$

$$= \left[3x+3x^2-\frac{x^3}{3}\right]_{1}^{5}$$

$$= \left(15+75-\frac{125}{3}\right)-\left(3+3-\frac{1}{3}\right)$$

$$= 48\frac{1}{3}-5\frac{2}{3} = 42\frac{2}{3}$$

Area under 'bottom' curve $= \int_{1}^{5}\left(13-6x+x^2\right)dx$

$$= \left[13x-3x^2+\frac{x^3}{3}\right]_{1}^{5}$$

$$= \left(65-75+\frac{125}{3}\right)-\left(13-3+\frac{1}{3}\right)$$

$$= 31\frac{2}{3}-10\frac{1}{3} = 21\frac{1}{3}$$

Total area $= 42\frac{2}{3}-21\frac{1}{3} = 21\frac{1}{3}$ units^2

Method 2

Area $= \int_{1}^{5}\left(\left(3+6x-x^2\right)-\left(13-6x+x^2\right)\right)dx$

$$= \int_{1}^{5}\left(3-13+6x+6x-x^2-x^2\right)dx$$

$$= \int_{1}^{5}\left(-10+12x-2x^2\right)dx$$

$$= \left[-10x+6x^2-\frac{2x^3}{3}\right]_{1}^{5}$$

$$= \left(-50+150-\frac{250}{3}\right)-\left(-10+6-\frac{2}{3}\right)$$

$$= \frac{50}{3}-\left(-4\frac{2}{3}\right) = 16\frac{2}{3}+4\frac{2}{3} = 21\frac{1}{3} \text{ units}^2$$

⭐ ■ $\int_{a}^{b}f'(x)dx = \left[f(x)\right]_{a}^{b} = f(b)-f(a)$

■ The area between the two lines $x=a$ and $x=b$, the x-axis and the curve $y=f(x)$ is $\int_{a}^{b}f(x)\,dx$.

■ The area between two curves is $\int_{a}^{b}\left(y_2-y_1\right)dx$.

■ If the curve lies under the x-axis then the area will be negative.

⚠ ■ If the curve crosses the x-axis in between the vertical lines, then the value of the integral will not be the area, as some parts will be positive and some will be negative.

■ If you are asked to find a definite integral not in the context of a problem then units will not be required. If the integral is within the context of a problem then units are required.

Exercise 4.5

1 Find the area between the curve $y=5+4x-x^2$, the x-axis and the lines $x=2$ and $x=4$.

2 Find the area enclosed by the curve $y=3+2x-x^2$ and the x-axis.

3 Show that the line $x+y=4$ cuts the curve $y=7-5x+x^2$ at A and B, where the co-ordinates of A and B are $(1, 3)$ and $(3, 1)$ respectively. Find the area enclosed.

4 Find the area enclosed between the curves $y=2+4x-x^2$ and $y=10-6x+x^2$.

6 Kinematics

Application to kinematics	c16	Be able to use differentiation and integration with respect to time to solve simple problems involving variable acceleration.
	c17	Be able to recognise the special case where the use of constant acceleration formulae is appropriate.
	c18	Be able to solve problems using these formulae.

Student's Book pages 213–231

Differentiation concerns rate of change. The rate of change of displacement of a body that is moving is called the velocity. The rate of change of velocity is acceleration. These three aspects of the motion of a body are related by calculus.

Use of words

Acceleration is a vector quantity. That means that it has magnitude and direction. In this specification we usually talk about motion along a straight line. Acceleration along the line can be negative. A negative acceleration can be called retardation or deceleration. If the acceleration, a, is -2 then you can say that there is a deceleration of 2.

Velocity is also a vector quantity, so the velocity of a body can be negative. If motion along a line remains in the same direction then velocity can also be called speed. Speed cannot be negative.

The distance travelled along the line in the positive direction is called the displacement. If motion remains in the same direction then displacement is interchangeable with distance. Displacement can be negative, whereas distance cannot be negative.

Example: A car travels at 60 mph northwards along a motorway for one hour and then travels at 60 mph southwards for an hour to return to its starting place. Find the average speed and the average velocity.

Answer: The total distance travelled is 120 miles, but the displacement is 0. The velocity for the first hour is 60 mph but the velocity for the second hour is −60 mph.

The average speed for the two hours $= \dfrac{\text{total distance}}{\text{total time}} = \dfrac{120}{2} = 60$ mph.

The average velocity for the two hours $= \dfrac{\text{displacement}}{\text{total time}} = \dfrac{0}{2} = 0$ mph.

Constant acceleration

If, at time t seconds, the displacement from a chosen start point is s metres, the initial velocity was u metres per second and the current velocity is v metres per second, then the following formulae connect these values. These formulae are **not** on the formula sheet and so need to be learned.

$$v = u + at \qquad s = \left(\frac{u+v}{2}\right)t$$

$$s = ut + \tfrac{1}{2}at^2 \qquad v^2 = u^2 + 2as$$

Example: A car decelerates uniformly from $15\,\mathrm{m\,s^{-1}}$ to rest in 10 seconds. Find the deceleration and the distance travelled.

Answer: In this example $u = 15$, $v = 0$ and $t = 10$.

To find the distance use $s = \left(\dfrac{u+v}{2}\right)t$.

$$\Rightarrow \quad s = \left(\frac{15+0}{2}\right)10 = 75$$

To find the acceleration use $v = u + at$.

$$\Rightarrow \quad 0 = 15 + 10a$$
$$\Rightarrow \quad a = -1.5$$

So the deceleration is $1.5\,\mathrm{m\,s^{-2}}$ and the distance is $75\,\mathrm{m}$.
Alternatively, start by using $v = u + at$.

$$\Rightarrow \quad 0 = 15 + 10a$$
$$\Rightarrow \quad a = -1.5$$

Now use $v^2 = u^2 + 2as$.

$$\Rightarrow \quad 0 = 15^2 - 3s$$
$$\Rightarrow \quad s = 75$$

Example: A car accelerates from rest along a road at $2\,\mathrm{ms^{-2}}$. Find how far it has travelled in the first 5 seconds of motion and the velocity at that time.

Answer: In this example $a = 2, u = 0$ and $t = 5$.

To find the distance use $s = ut + \frac{1}{2}at^2$.

$$\Rightarrow \quad s = 0 + \frac{1}{2} \times 2 \times 5^2 = 25$$

To find the velocity use $v = u + at$.

$$\Rightarrow \quad v = 0 + 2 \times 5 = 10$$

The displacement is 25 metres and the velocity is 10 metres per second.

Acceleration due to gravity

Bodies that fall freely are under the influence of gravity, which gives a constant acceleration. The letter g is used to represent gravitational acceleration. In these situations the value of g will be provided (usually $9.8\,\mathrm{m\,s^{-2}}$).

Example: A ball is dropped from a window 30 metres above the ground. How long does it take for the ball to reach the ground and with what velocity does it land? (Take $g = 9.8\,\mathrm{ms^{-2}}$.)

Answer: In this example $a = 9.8$, $u = 0$ and $s = 30$.

To find the time use $s = ut + \frac{1}{2}at^2$.

$$\Rightarrow \quad 30 = 0 + \frac{1}{2} \times 9.8 \times t^2$$
$$\Rightarrow \quad t^2 = 6.12$$
$$\Rightarrow \quad t = 2.47$$

To find the velocity use $v^2 = u^2 + 2as$.

$$\Rightarrow \quad v^2 = 0 + 2 \times 9.8 \times 30 = 588$$
$$\Rightarrow \quad v = 24.2$$

The time is 2.47 seconds and the velocity is 24.2 metres per second.

 Remember to give your answers correct to 3 significant figures unless instructed otherwise.

Variable acceleration

If acceleration is not constant, then it is a function of time. Velocity and displacement are also then functions of time.

Since velocity is rate of change of displacement and acceleration is rate of change of velocity, to find one given the other you either differentiate or integrate.

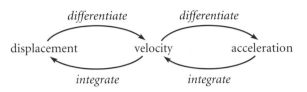

Example: A body moves along a straight line. As it passes a point O it is travelling at 4 ms^{-1}.
The acceleration t seconds after passing O is given by $a = 2 + t$.
Find the velocity after 5 seconds and the displacement at that time.

Answer: Velocity is found by integrating as the acceleration is not constant.

$$a = 2 + t \implies v = 2t + \frac{t^2}{2} + c$$

When $t = 0, v = 4 \implies c = 4$

$$\implies v = 2t + \frac{t^2}{2} + 4$$

Displacement is found by integrating.

$$v = 2t + \frac{t^2}{2} + 4 \implies s = t^2 + \frac{t^3}{6} + 4t + c$$

When $t = 0, s = 0 \implies c = 0$

$$\implies s = t^2 + \frac{t^3}{6} + 4t$$

When $t = 5, v = 10 + \frac{25}{2} + 4 = 26\frac{1}{2}$

$$\implies s = 25 + \frac{125}{6} + 20 = 65\frac{5}{6}$$

The velocity is 26.5 ms^{-1} and the displacement is 65.8 m.

⚠️ ■ Remember the difference between speed and velocity and between distance and displacement.
■ Remember the difference between constant acceleration and variable acceleration. If acceleration is given as a function of t then it is not constant.
■ The formulae for constant acceleration are **not** given on the formula sheet in the exam and must be learned.

⭐ ■ If displacement is given as a function of time, then differentiate to find the velocity and differentiate again to find the acceleration.
■ If acceleration is given as a function of time, then integrate to find the velocity and integrate again to find the displacement. Do not forget the constants of integration.

Exercise 4.6

1 A particle moves in a straight line with a constant acceleration of 2 ms^{-2}. At a point O it has a velocity of 4 ms^{-1}. Find its displacement and velocity 4 seconds after passing O.

2 A car travelling at 30 ms^{-1} passes a point A on a motorway. It slows at a constant rate so that 10 seconds later it is travelling at 15 ms^{-1}. Find the deceleration and the distance travelled in this time.

3 A body moves along a straight line with acceleration given by $a = 2 - t$. As it passes a point O it is travelling with velocity 8 ms^{-1}. Find the velocity and the displacement after 6 seconds.

4 A particle moves along a straight line. t seconds after passing point O, the displacement s metres is given by $s = 9t^2 - t^3$. Find the time, other than $t = 0$, at which the particle is instantaneously at rest and the displacement at this time. What happens after this time?

1 Find $\int_{1}^{3}(x^2 - x)\,\mathrm{d}x$. [4]

2 (i) Show that there is a stationary point at $(1, 9)$ on the curve $y = x^3 - 6x^2 + 9x + 5$ and
determine the nature of this stationary point. [5]

(ii) Find the co-ordinates of the other stationary point and hence sketch the curve. [2]

[OCR 2003 Q2]

3 The gradient function of a curve is given by $\dfrac{\mathrm{d}y}{\mathrm{d}x} = 2 + 2x - x^2$. Find the equation of the curve
given that it passes through the point $(3, 10)$. [4]

[OCR 2003 Q3]

4 A car, which is initially travelling at $20\ \mathrm{ms}^{-1}$, accelerates uniformly at $1.2\ \mathrm{ms}^{-2}$.
Find

(i) the speed after 5 seconds [2]

(ii) the distance travelled in this time. [2]

[OCR 2003 Q10]

5 The curve shown is part of the graph of $y = 4 - x^2$.

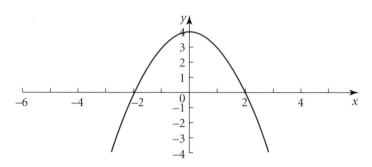

Calculate the area of the region between this curve and the x-axis, giving your answer
as an exact fraction. [4]

[OCR 2004 Q2]

6 A car starts from rest and reaches $20\ \mathrm{ms}^{-1}$ in 8 seconds.

(a) Jane models the motion of the car by assuming constant acceleration during the first 8 seconds.

(i) Find the value of the constant acceleration. [2]

(ii) Find the distance travelled during this time. [2]

(b) Paul claims that constant acceleration is not a good model in this situation.

He uses the following formula for the velocity, $v\ \mathrm{ms}^{-1}$, at time t seconds for the first 8 seconds
of motion.

$$v = \frac{60t^2 - 5t^3}{64}$$

(i) Show that this formula does give $v = 0$ when $t = 0$ and $v = 20$ when $t = 8$. [1]

(ii) Find the acceleration when $t = 8$. [3]

(iii) Find the distance travelled during the first 8 seconds using this model. [4]

[OCR 2004 Q14]

Answers

Section 1

Exercise 1.1 (page 3)

1 (i) $2x + y$

(ii) x

(iii) $6y$

2 (i) $8a + b$

(ii) $3x^2 + 8x$

(iii) $2x^2 + x - 3$

3 (i) $2(x + 2y)$

(ii) $x(x + 3y)$

(iii) $2xy(y + 3x)$

4 (i) $\dfrac{3x}{4}$

(ii) $\dfrac{1 - x}{(x + 1)(x + 2)}$

5 $a = \dfrac{2s - 2ut}{t^2}$

6 (i) $x = \dfrac{6}{5}$

(ii) $x = -5$

(iii) $x = \dfrac{5}{7}$

Exercise 1.2 (page 5)

1 (i) $x = 2$ or $x = -5$

(ii) $x = 4$ or $x = -1$

(iii) $x = 5$ or $x = 1$

2 (i) $x = 4.70$ or $x = -1.70$

(ii) $x = 3.45$ or $x = -1.45$

(iii) $x = -4.24$ or $x = 0.236$

3 $f(x) = (x + 3)^2 + 1$
The minimum value of $f(x)$ is therefore 1 and so $f(x)=0$ has no roots.

4 (i) $x = \dfrac{5}{2}$ or $x = \dfrac{1}{4}$

(ii) $x = -2.35$ or $x = 0.851$

5 $f(x) = 6 - (x - 2)^2$
The maximum value of $f(x)$ is 6, when $x=2$.

Exercise 1.3 (page 7)

1 $x = 2, y = -3$

2 $x = 3, y = 2$

3 $x = 5, y = 5$ and $x = 1, y = 7$

4 $(1.59, 4.18), (-2.39, -3.78)$

Exercise 1.4 (page 9)

1 $50°, 60°, 70°$

2 4 and 6 people

3 80 km/h and 90 km/h

4 £1.05, £1.78

Exercise 1.5 (page 11)

1 $x > 2$

2 $x < -\dfrac{1}{4}$

3 $x > 2$ or $x < -4$

Exercise 1.6 (page 13)

1 (i) $x^3 + 2x^2 - 4x + 2$

(ii) $x^3 + 2x^2 - 2x$

(iii) $2x^3 + 2x^2 + 5x + 9$

2 $2x^3 - 3x^2 - 5x + 6$

3 $x^2 + x + 1$ with remainder -4

4 (i) 6

(ii) -14

5 (i) $f(2) = 0$

(ii) $f(-1) = 0$

6 Factors can only be $\pm 1, \pm 3$;
$f(3) = 0$
$\Rightarrow (x - 1)(x + 1)(x - 3) = 0$
$\Rightarrow x = -1, x = 1,$ or $x = 3$

Exercise 1.7 (page 15)

1 $1 + 6x + 15x^2 + 20x^3$

2 6

3 $10\left(\dfrac{5}{6}\right)^3 \left(\dfrac{1}{6}\right)^2 = 0.161$

4 0.999

Exam practice Section 1 (page 16)

1 (i) $8(x - 1) - 24 = 3(3x + 1)$
$\Rightarrow 8x - 8 - 24 = 9x + 3$
$\Rightarrow 8x - 9x = 8 + 24 + 3$
$\Rightarrow -x = 35$
$\Rightarrow x = -35$

(ii) $x = \dfrac{4 \pm \sqrt{16 + 28}}{2}$
$= \dfrac{4 \pm \sqrt{44}}{2}$
$= 2 \pm \sqrt{11}$
$\Rightarrow x = 5.32$ or $x = -1.32$

2 (i) $3 - x > 5(x + 1)$
$\Rightarrow 3 - x > 5x + 5$
$\Rightarrow -2 > 6x$
$\Rightarrow x < -\dfrac{1}{3}$

(ii) $x^2 - 5x < 6$
$\Rightarrow x^2 - 5x - 6 < 0$
$\Rightarrow (x - 6)(x + 1) < 0$
$\Rightarrow -1 < x < 6$

3 (i) $f(x) = (x - 3)^2 - 9 - 10$
$= (x - 3)^2 - 19$

(ii) The minimum value of $f(x)$ is -19, when $x = 3$.

(iii) $(x - 3)^2 = 19$
$\Rightarrow x - 3 = \pm\sqrt{19}$
$\Rightarrow \quad x = 3 \pm \sqrt{19}$
$\Rightarrow \quad x = 7.36$ or $x = -1.36$

4 $x + 6 = x^2 - x + 3$
$\Rightarrow x^2 - 2x - 3 = 0$
$\Rightarrow (x - 3)(x + 1) = 0$
$\Rightarrow x = 3, y = 9$ and $x = -1, y = 5$
Alternatively eliminate x, giving
$y^2 - 14y + 45 = 0$
$\Rightarrow (y - 9)(y - 5) = 0$
$\Rightarrow y = 9, x = 3$ and $y = 5, x = -1$

5 (i) $f(3) = 27 + 18 - 15 - 6 = 24$

(ii) $f(2) = 8 + 8 - 10 - 6 = 0$

(iii) Factorise $f(x)$.
$f(x) = (x - 2)(x^2 + 4x + 3)$
$x^2 + 4x + 3 = (x + 3)(x + 1)$
$\Rightarrow f(x) = (x - 2)(x + 3)(x + 1)$
So $f(x) = 0$ gives $x = 2, x = -3$ or $x = -1$.

6 (i) $(2 + x)^7$
$= 2^7 + 7 \times 2^6 x + 21 \times 2^5 x^2 + 35 \times 2^4 x^3 + \dots$
$= 128 + 448x + 672x^2 + 560x^3 + \dots$

(ii) Substitute $x = -0.01$
$\Rightarrow 1.99^7 = 128 - 4.48 + 0.0672 - 0.000560 + \dots = 123.5866$

7 (i) Time during the day $= \dfrac{200}{v}$
Time during the night $= \dfrac{200}{v + 20}$

(ii) $\dfrac{200}{v} - \dfrac{200}{v + 20} = \dfrac{50}{60}$
$\Rightarrow 200(v + 20) - 200v = \dfrac{5}{6}v(v + 20)$
$\Rightarrow 4000 \times 6 = 5v(v + 20)$
$\Rightarrow 5v^2 + 100v = 24000$
$\Rightarrow v^2 + 20v - 4800 = 0$

(iii) $\Rightarrow (v + 80)(v - 60) = 0$
$\Rightarrow v = 60$ or $v - 80$ (reject)
$\Rightarrow$ day speed $= 60$
$\Rightarrow$ day time $= \dfrac{200}{60}$
$= 3$ hrs 20 mins
$\Rightarrow$ night speed $= 80$
$\Rightarrow$ night time $= \dfrac{200}{80}$
$= 2$ hrs 30 mins

8 (i) $\left(\dfrac{5}{6}\right)^5 = 0.402$

(ii) $1 - \left(\dfrac{5}{6}\right)^5 = 1 - 0.402 = 0.598$

(iii) $\binom{5}{3}\left(\dfrac{5}{6}\right)^2 \left(\dfrac{1}{6}\right)^3 = 0.0322$

Section 2

Exercise 2.1 (page 20)

1 (i) 2

(ii) $\frac{1}{2}$

(iii) $-\frac{2}{3}$

2 (i) $x + 2y = 16$

(ii) $2x - y = 2$

3 Gradient of AB = gradient of CD = $\frac{4}{3}$

So AB and CD are parallel.

Gradient of AD and BC are parallel $-\frac{3}{4}$.

So AD and BC are parallel.

Since $=-\frac{3}{4} \times \frac{4}{3} = -1$, AB and AD are perpendicular.

So ABCD is a rectangle.

4 (i) $(4, 4)$

(ii) $\sqrt{40} = 2\sqrt{10} \approx 6.32$

5 (i) $y = x - 2$

(ii) $y + 3x = 15$

6

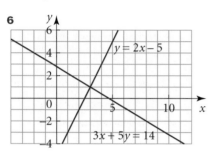

The lines intersect at $(3, 1)$.

Exercise 2.2 (page 21)

1 $x^2 + y^2 = 9$

2 $(x-2)^2 + (y-1)^2 = 9$

3 Rearrange in the form
$(x+3)^2 - 9 + (y-2)^2 - 4 - 8 = 0$
$\Rightarrow (x+3)^2 + (y-2)^2 = 21$
$\Rightarrow$ Centre $(-3, 2)$, radius $\sqrt{21}$

4 Outside: circle has centre $(3, 1)$ and radius 2; distance of point from centre is $\sqrt{5} > 2$.

Exercise 2.3 (page 25)

1

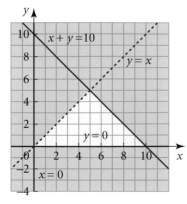

2 (i)

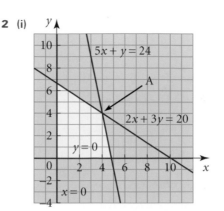

(ii) Maximum value of P is when the line $P = 4x + y$ passes through the point A which is $(4, 4)$. So $P = 20$.

3 (i)

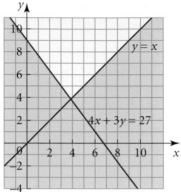

(ii) The minimum value of P would be at the intersection, except that this is not an integer point. The nearest point to this is $(4, 4)$ giving $P = 32$. (The next nearest point is $(3, 5)$ giving $P = 34$.)

4 $12x + 30y \geqslant 120$
$x + y \leqslant 8$

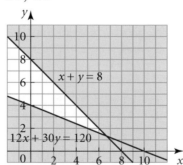

(i) 6 minibuses and 2 coaches (with 12 spare seats)

(ii) 4 coaches

Exam practice Section 2 (page 26)

1 (i) Gradient of AC $= \frac{-3-0}{7-(-2)}$

$= \frac{-3}{9} = -\frac{1}{3}$

Gradient of BD $= \frac{-4-2}{0-2}$

$= \frac{-6}{-2} = 3$

Since $3 \times -\frac{1}{3} = -1$
the lines are perpendicular.

(ii) Midpoint of BD

$= \left(\frac{2+0}{2}, \frac{2+(-4)}{2} \right)$

$= (1, -1)$

Gradient of AM $= \frac{-1-0}{1-(-2)}$

$= -\frac{1}{3}$ = gradient of AC

$\Rightarrow$ points are collinear.

(Alternatively, the equation of AC is $x + 3y + 2 = 0$.
This equation is satisfied by $(1, -1)$ as $1 - 3 + 2 = 0$.)

2 (i) First line: $y = -2x + 4$
Second line: $y = -2x + \frac{5}{2}$
Therefore gradients are the same and the lines are parallel.
(Alternatively, attempting to solve the equations simultaneously to find their point of intersection leads to an impossibility, e.g. $8 = 5$, showing that the lines do not cross and hence are parallel.)

(ii) Perpendicular line has gradient $\frac{1}{2}$

$\Rightarrow y - 6 = \frac{1}{2}(x - 1)$

$\Rightarrow 2y - x = 11$

3 (i) $(x-1)^2 + (y-2)^2 = 25$;
centre $(1, 2)$, radius 5

(ii) Substitute: $(x-1)^2 + x^2 = 25$
$\Rightarrow 2x^2 - 2x - 24 = 0$
$\Rightarrow x^2 - x - 12 = 0$
$\Rightarrow (x-4)(x+3) = 0$
$\Rightarrow x = 4$ or $x = -3$
$\Rightarrow (4,6), (-3,-1)$

(iii) AC = BC = 5, AB = $7\sqrt{2}$

$\Rightarrow$ angle $= 2 \times \sin^{-1}\left(\frac{\frac{7}{2}\sqrt{2}}{5} \right)$

$= 2 \times \sin^{-1}(0.99)$

$= 2 \times 81.87°$

$\Rightarrow$ ACB $= 163.7°$

4 (i)

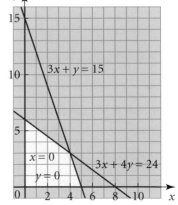

(ii) The lines meet at $(4, 3)$.
Maximum value of $2x + y$ is 11.

Answers

5 (i) $18x + 11y \le 200$

$7x + 6y \le 84$

$x \ge 2$

$y \ge 2$

(ii)

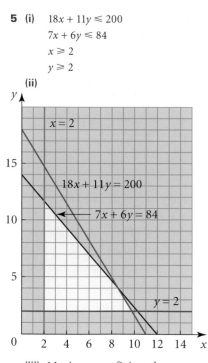

(iii) Maximum profit is at the intersection of the lines:

$P = 70x + 50y$.

Nearest integer point to it is (9, 3)

$\Rightarrow$ 9 components of type X and 3 of type Y; profit is £780.

Section 3

Exercise 3.1 (page 29)

1 $\tan\theta = -0.625$,

$\sin\theta = 0.530$,

$\cos\theta = -0.848$.

2 Principal Angle = $44.4°$,

second angle = $180° - 44.4°$,

$\theta = 135.6°$.

3 Principal Angle = $-50.2°$. The angles in the given range are in the second and fourth quadrants and so are $360° - 50.2° = 309.8°$ and $180° - 50.2° = 129.8°$.

4 $\cos 2\theta = 0.7$

$\Rightarrow 2\theta = 45.6°$ and $314.4°$

and also $2\theta = 405.6°$

and also $2\theta = 674.4°$

$\Rightarrow \theta = 22.8°, 157.2°, 202.8°$ and $337.2°$

Exercise 3.2 (page 31)

1 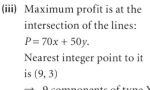 $\dfrac{\sqrt{21}}{5}$

2 The equation is $\tan\theta = \dfrac{7}{4}$.

$\Rightarrow \theta = 60.3°$ and $\theta = 240.3°$

3 The equation is

$3\sin^2\theta + \sin\theta - 1 = 0$

$\Rightarrow \theta = 25.7°, 154.3°, 230.1°, 309.9°$

Exercise 3.3 (page 33)

1 $a = 5.88$, area = 17.6

2 $Q = 31.0°$

3 $102.6°, 32.2°, 45.2°$

Exercise 3.4 (page 35)

1 (i) $EBC = 33.7°$

(ii) $EAC = 18.9°$

2 Angle EBC is the angle of greatest slope.

Exam practice Section 3 (page 36)

1 $\sin 2x = 0.5$

$\Rightarrow 2x = 30°$ and $150°$

and also $2x = 390°$

and also $2x = 510°$

$\Rightarrow x = 15°, 75°, 195°, 255°$

2 (i) $\cos^2\theta = 1 - \sin^2\theta$

$\Rightarrow 2 - 2\sin^2\theta + \sin\theta = 2$

$\Rightarrow 2\sin^2\theta - \sin\theta = 0$

(ii) $2\sin^2\theta - \sin\theta = 0$

$\Rightarrow \sin\theta\,(2\sin\theta - 1) = 0$

$\Rightarrow \sin\theta = 0$ or $\sin\theta = \dfrac{1}{2}$

$\Rightarrow \theta = 0°, 30°, 150°, 180°$

3 $\sin x = 3\cos x$

$\Rightarrow \tan x = 3$

$\Rightarrow x = 71.6°$ and $251.6°$

4 LHS $= 1 + \tan^2\theta = 1 + \dfrac{b^2}{a^2}$

$= \dfrac{a^2 + b^2}{a^2} = \dfrac{c^2}{a^2}$

$= \dfrac{1}{\cos^2\theta} =$ RHS

5 $AB = 6$

$\Rightarrow AC = 6\sqrt{2} \approx 8.485$

$\Rightarrow AO = 3\sqrt{2} \approx 4.243$

$\Rightarrow \tan\theta = \dfrac{7}{3\sqrt{2}} \approx 1.650$

$\Rightarrow \theta = 58.8°$

6 (i) From calculator, $\tan^{-1}0.75 = 36.9°$. But $\cos 36.9° = +0.8$. There is a second angle in the third quadrant, where the cosine value is negative i.e. $x = 180° + 36.9° = 216.9°$

(ii) $\tan x = -2$

$\Rightarrow x = 116.6°$ or $x = 296.6°$

Section 4

Exercise 4.1 (page 38)

1 (i) $\dfrac{dy}{dx} = 2x + 1$

(ii) $\dfrac{dy}{dx} = 6x^2 + 3$

2 0

3 -4

Exercise 4.2 (page 40)

1 $y = 13x - 19$

2 $5y + x = 11$

3 $(5, 22)$

4 $(0, -4)$ and $(2, 4)$

5 6

Exercise 4.3 (page 43)

1 Maximum at $(1, 0)$;

minimum at $\left(\dfrac{5}{3}, \dfrac{-4}{27}\right)$.

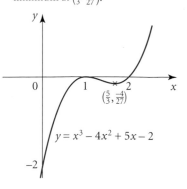

2 (ii) 25

3 $\dfrac{dy}{dx} = 3x^2 + 2x + 1$

In this quadratic expression, '$b^2 - 4ac$'< 0, so there are no roots and $\dfrac{dy}{dx}$ is never 0. Hence there are no turning points.

Exercise 4.4 (page 45)

1 (i) $\dfrac{x^8}{8} + c$

(ii) $\dfrac{5x^4}{4} + \dfrac{x^6}{2} + c$

(iii) $\dfrac{2x^3}{3} - \dfrac{x^2}{2} + c$

2 $y = \dfrac{x^3}{3} + x^2 - 3x + c$

3 $y = x^2 - 5x + 6$

4 (i) $x^3 - 2x^2 + x + c$

(ii) $\dfrac{2x^3}{3} - \dfrac{x^2}{2} + c$

(iii) $\dfrac{2x^3}{3} - \dfrac{x^2}{2} - 3x + c$

Exercise 4.5 (page 48)

1 $\dfrac{46}{3}$ units²

2 $\dfrac{32}{3}$ units²

3 $\dfrac{4}{3}$ units²

4 9 units²

Exercise 4.6 (page 51)

1 $s = 32\,\text{m}, v = 12\,\text{m s}^{-1}$

2 $a = -1.5\,\text{m s}^{-2}, s = 225\,\text{m}$

3 $v = 2\,\text{ms}^{-1}$

$s = 48\,\text{m}$

4 $v = 0$ when $t = 0$ and $t = 6$

After this time, v becomes negative, meaning that the particle begins to return towards O.

At this time $s = 108\,\text{m}$

Exam practice Section 4

(page 52)

1 $\int_1^3 (x^2 - x)\,dx = \left[\dfrac{x^3}{3} - \dfrac{x^2}{2}\right]_1^3$

$= \left(9 - \dfrac{9}{2}\right) - \left(\dfrac{1}{3} - \dfrac{1}{2}\right)$

$= \dfrac{9}{2} - \left(-\dfrac{1}{6}\right)$

$= \dfrac{14}{3}$

2 (i) $\dfrac{dy}{dx} = 3x^2 - 12x + 9 = 0$

when $x^2 - 4x + 3 = 0$

$\Rightarrow (x - 3)(x - 1) = 0$

$\Rightarrow x = 1 \Rightarrow y = 9$

$\dfrac{d^2y}{dx^2} = 6x - 12 < 0$

when $x = 1 \Rightarrow$ maximum

(ii) $(3, 5)$

$y = x^3 - 6x^2 + 9x + 5$

3 $\dfrac{dy}{dx} = 2 + 2x - x^2$

$\Rightarrow y = 2x + x^2 - \dfrac{x^3}{3} + c$

Substitute $x = 3$ and $y = 10$.

$\Rightarrow 10 = 6 + 9 - 9 + c$

$\Rightarrow c = 4$

$\Rightarrow y = 2x + x^2 - \dfrac{x^3}{3} + 4$

4 (i) $v = u + at$

$\Rightarrow v = 20 + 1.2 \times 5$

$= 26\,\text{ms}^{-1}$

(ii) $s = ut + \dfrac{1}{2}at^2$

$\Rightarrow s = 100 + 0.6 \times 25 = 115\,\text{m}$

5 Area $= \displaystyle\int_{-2}^2 (4 - x^2)\,dx$

$= \left[4x - \dfrac{x^3}{3}\right]_{-2}^2$

$= \left(8 - \dfrac{8}{3}\right) - \left(-8 - \dfrac{-8}{3}\right)$

$= 16 - \dfrac{16}{3} = \dfrac{32}{3}$ units^2

6 (a) (i) $v = at$

$\Rightarrow a = \dfrac{20}{8} = 2.5\,\text{ms}^{-2}$

(ii) $s = \dfrac{1}{2}at^2 \Rightarrow s = 80\,\text{m}$

(b) (i) Substitute

$t = 0$ to give $v = 0$

and $t = 8$ to give $v = 20$

(ii) Differentiate:

$a = \dfrac{dv}{dt} = \dfrac{120t - 15t^2}{64}$

When $t = 8$, $a = 0$

(iii) Integrate:

$s = \displaystyle\int_0^8 \left(\dfrac{60t^2 - 5t^3}{64}\right)dt$

$= \left[\dfrac{20t^3 - \frac{5}{4}t^4}{64}\right]_0^8$

$= \left(\dfrac{10\,240 - 5120}{64}\right) = 80\,\text{m}$